THE HIBS QUIZ BOOK

THE
HIBS
QUIZ BOOK

JIM HOSSACK

MAINSTREAM
PUBLISHING

Copyright © Jim Hossack, 1988

All rights reserved
First published in Great Britain in 1988 by
MAINSTREAM PUBLISHING COMPANY (EDINBURGH) LTD
7 Albany Street
Edinburgh EH1 3UG

ISBN 1 85158 183 9 (paper)

British Library Cataloguing in Publication Data
Hossack, Jim
    The Hibs quiz book.
    1. Scotland. Association football. Clubs :
    Hibernian Football club – to 1988.
    I. Title
    796.334′63′094134

    ISBN 1 85158 183 9

Typeset in 11/13 Imprint by Bookworm Typesetting Ltd, Edinburgh
Printed in Great Britain by Butler & Tanner Ltd, Frome

ACKNOWLEDGEMENTS

The compiler would like to thank the following for their help:

My long-suffering wife, Margaret, for her endless support and understanding.

A very special thank you to my long-time friend and fellow Hibee, Pat Higney, whose knowledge of the club, enthusiastic help and encouragement have been invaluable and greatly appreciated.

A big thank you to the *Glasgow Herald*, in particular Harry Reid and Jim McNeish, for their assistance and kind permission to reproduce many of the photographs in this book.

Niall Kennedy at the Strathclyde Programme Shop.

My pals, John Melrose and Ian Armour . . . Thanks, lads!

Jim Gray, Hibernian's managing director, for doing me the honour of writing the book's Foreword.

. . . And last, but not least, Bill Campbell of Mainstream Publishing for giving me the opportunity to walk down memory lane with my beloved Hibees.

FOREWORD

HIBERNIAN FOOTBALL CLUB have a history as pioneers in football. This famous club have led the way with ideas which are now accepted as commonplace in the modern game, with concepts such as European involvement, undersoil heating and shirt sponsorship. Such was the foresight of the previous directors of the club.

With such an involvement in the history of football, notwithstanding the current club's re-emergence story, it is the perfect subject matter for an exciting and stimulating *Quiz Book*. I know the author, Jim Hossack, and not only did he inform David Duff and I of many new facts, albeit we have supported the club since childhood, he has a great love for the "Hibs" and a wealth of knowledge I doubt can be found elsewhere.

Who better to compile questions to stimulate memories that will cover the years from Queen Victoria's reign to the present day and embrace teams including Hugh Shaw, Willie Harper, from the early years, Younger, Turnbull, Smith, Reilly, Smith and Johnstone from the recent past and modern day heroes ranging from Baker, Cormack, Stanton, Edwards, Cropley and O'Rourke? The list of idols, in fact, is endless; after all, every supporter has their own favourite.

Our current players will, I trust become the heroes of the future and success for the team will guarantee that honour. Meantime I trust you will enjoy your journey into our history and no doubt you will recall many happy memories associated with Hibernian Football Club.

JAMES C GRAY
Managing Director

Questions

1 Who, at an August 1987 press conference, accurately described Hibernian as being "The greatest football club on Earth"?

KICK-OFF

2 In which year were Hibernian founded?

3 What is their highest home League win and against whom?

4 What is their highest away League win and against whom?

5 Which club did Hibs beat 15-1 in a 1961 Scottish Cup tie to record their biggest win in the competition?

6 What is the club's highest victory in any recorded match?

7 In which years did Hibernian win the Scottish cup?

8 How many times have they been beaten finalists?

9 How often have "The Hibees" been League Champions (top division)?

10 In which season did they win the League by ten clear points?

11 In which season did they score most League goals, and how many?

12 In which season did Hibs attain their highest points total?

13 Which player has scored most goals for the club (all matches)?

14 In which season did they win the Scottish League Cup?

15 Which player has made most League appearances for Hibs?

16 Who scored Hibs' first ever Premier League goal?

17 In 1947-48 Hibernian became the first East of Scotland club to win the Championship for 45 years. What was the points difference between the Champs and second-placed Rangers?

18 Where did Hibs clinch their 1950/51 title with a 4-0 win?

19 Hibernian were Champions again in 1951/52. Which team did they beat 3-1 at Easter Road to clinch that title?

FRESH IN THE MEMORY

Events from the start of season 1987/88 to August 1988

20 From which club did Hibs sign Gareth Evans and for which English First Division side did he once play?

21 Against which club did Evans make a scoring debut in February 1988?

22 Which club did Mickey Weir join in September 1987 and what was the fee set by an October tribunal?

23 Against which club did Weir play his last game before leaving Easter Road?

24 Where did Mickey make his first appearance on returning to his favourite club in January 1988?

25 Against which club did Hibs draw all four Premier League fixtures in season 1987/88?

26 Which club did Alan Rough join after being released in the Spring of 1988?

27 Who were Hibs' opponents in the first round of the 1987/88 Skol Cup, and what was the score?

28 Which team did Hibs beat 3-1 in the following round, and who made his debut in that match?

29 Which team knocked Hibs out of the Skol Cup in season 1987/88 and who made his debut in that match?

30 Who scored Hibernian's first competitive goal of season 1987/88 and what was the match result?

31 Can you name the 1987/88 Premier League goalkeeping opponent whose dad once played in the same position for Hibs?

32 Which club did Hibernian beat in both Premier League fixtures played away from home?

33 Where and when did Graham Mitchell score his only Premier League goal in season 1987/88?

34 Who scored Hibs' penalty equaliser v Rangers at Ibrox in April 1988?

35 Who scored Hibernian's equaliser in the 1-1 draw with Celtic at Parkhead in October 1987?

36 Why was Wednesday, 12 August 1987 glorious for Hibs and their fans?

37 Who scored the all-important goal in the above match?
38 Who scored Hibs' goals in the 2-0 victory over Aberdeen at Pittodrie on 4 May 1988?
39 Can you name the English club to which midfield player Dougie Bell was transferred in season 1987/88?
40 Against which team did Bell score his only Premier League goal of the season before heading south?
41 Why did the *Sunday Mail* describe events at the Hibs v Morton match on 7 May 1988 as "The craziest scenes ever seen in the Premier League"?
42 Can you name the lady who, in September 1987, became the first female director of the club?
43 In May 1988 Hibernian signed a lucrative sponsorship deal with the Frank Graham Group. How much is it worth to the club over three years?
44 Which prestigious award did John Collins win in May 1988?
45 In February 1988 Hibs won three consecutive Premier League fixtures . . . who were the opponents and what were the match results?
46 Can you name the promising midfielder who made his first-team debut as a substitute when Morton were beaten 3-1 at Easter Road in May 1988?
47 In an ambitious move Hibs signed Steve Archibald in August 1988. name, in reverse order, the other senior clubs for which "Archie" has played.
48 On 28 July 1988 it was revealed that Hibernian would become the first Scottish club to go on the stock market. Can you name the only other British club whose shares are traded on the open market?

49 What was the reported fee paid to Oldham Athletic for the transfer of Andy Goram in October 1987?

50 Against which club did Goram make his Hibernian debut and what was the result of that match?

51 Andy played in 37 competitive matches during season 1987/88. How many shut-outs did he achieve? *A*: 16 *B*: 9 *C*: 13

N.B. Period or position specified where two or more players share the same surname.

52 . . . . Nutley.

53 . . . . Whiteford.

54 . . . . Cairns.

55 . . . . Byrne.

56 . . . . Kilgour.

57 . . . . Gartshore.

58 . . . . Brady.

59 . . . . McCreadie.

60 . . . . Hutchinson.

61 . . . . Ritchie.

62 . . . . Mulkerrin.

63 . . . . Muir. (1950's/1960's defender).

64 . . . . Bogie.

65 . . . . McGhee (1970's forward).

66 . . . . Hazel.

67 . . . . McLelland.

68 . . . . Caskie.

69 . . . . Stevenson (1960's left winger).

70 . . . . McNamee.

71 . . . . Wilson (1960's goalkeeper).

72 . . . . Peggie.

73 . . . . Murray (1980's player).

74 . . . . Adair.

75 . . . . Rae (1980's goalkeeper).

76 . . . . Whyte.

77 . . . . Barry.

78 . . . . Rodier.

79 . . . . Harrower (a club chairman).

80 . . . . Falconer.

81 . . . . Nicol.

82 . . . . Torrance.

83 . . . . Milne (famous 1930's and 1940's player).

84 . . . . Milne (1980's player).

85 . . . . Urquhart.

86 . . . . Laing.
87 . . . . Plumb.
88 . . . . Raisbeck.
89 . . . . Campbell.
90 . . . . Groves.
91 . . . . Pringle.
92 . . . . Templeton.
93 . . . . Temperley.
94 . . . . Tortolano.
95 . . . . O'Brien.
96 . . . . Graham.
97 . . . . Aitken.
98 . . . . Gallagher.
99 . . . . Simpson (1960's full-back).
100 . . . . Conroy.
101 . . . . McKee.

PICTURE QUIZ

102 Can you unmask these Hibees photographed in 1985?

103 Can you name the happy Hibees in this 1953 photograph?
104 Which player later became manager of the club?

DATELINE

To what events, which took place on the following dates, could these fictitious press headlines be referring?

105 4 August 1973 .... (A GORDON FOR ME!).
106 8 March 1986 .... (MAY DAY!).
107 9 December 1972 ...... (HIBS HAVE IT ALL OFF PAT!).
108 12 February 1887 . ('SONS' ROCKED BY HAPPY HIBS!).
109 28 October 1950 .... (WELL, WELL, WELL!).
110 1 January 1973 .... (SEVENTH HEAVEN!).
111 4 April 1956 .... (I HATE PARIS!).
112 9 October 1974 .... (CRUELTY TO 'BAIRNS'!).

113 26 April 1902 .... (THE BATTLE OF THE GREENS!).
114 2 January 1950 .... (STOP SHOVIN' JIMMY!).
115 17 October 1987 .... (KANE IS ABLE!).
116 18 April 1953 . (FOR HIBERNIAN AND SCOTLAND!).
117 27 March 1965 .. (HARDLY PAR FOR THE COURSE!).
118 29 November 1967 .... (NIGHTMARE FOR
                                                  NEAPOLITANS!).
119 24 November 1979 ...... (IRISH EYES ARE SMILING!).
120 16 December 1972 .... (EIGHTSOME REEL!).
121 17 September 1975 .... (KOP THAT!).
122 16 January 1971 .... (MANY HAPPY RETURNS!).
123 9 April 1958 .... (THEY'RE SINGIN' THE BLUES!).
124 10 October 1964 .. (IT'S THE REAL HIBS AT IBROX!).

PICTURE QUIZ

125 Can our older fans identify this international centre-half who
     played for both Hibs and Hearts in the 1940s?

126 Can you identify this early 1960's full-back?

127 To which club was he transferred in season 1962/63?

128 Which famous player scored the winning goal when the club first won the Scottish Cup by beating Dumbarton 2-1 in 1887?

129 What was the significance of Hibs' victory in that 1887 final?

130 Exactly 101 years later, in February 1988, Hibs met Dumbarton in a Scottish Cup tie replay. What was the match result?

131 Who scored the all-important goal when Hibs beat Celtic 1-0 in the 1902 final on the only other occasion on which the club has won the trophy?

132 Where was that 1902 final played, and why?

133 Eighty-six years later, in February 1988, Hibernian and Celtic met in a Scottish Cup tie replay. What was the match result?

134 Can you name the future Hibs player who scored the only goal of the game when Morton beat Hibernian in a replayed League Cup semi at Ibrox in October 1963?

135 Five years later the same player scored the winner for Hibs in a League Cup semi played at Tynecastle. Who were the opponents and what was the match result?

136 Can you name the player who scored against Aberdeen within the first 20 seconds of a 1972 Scottish Cup tie?

137 At which ground was the record attendance of 14,900 recorded when Hibernian were the visitors for a February 1965 Scottish Cup tie replay?

138 Hibs lost only one goal in the 1922/23 Scottish Cup competition. Where, and against whom?

139 1924, and Hibs are back in the final . . . who were the opponents and what was the match result?

140 Where was that 1924 final played, and how many Scottish Cup finals since that date have been staged at the same venue?

141 Amazingly the same eleven players represented the club in both the 1923 and 1924 finals . . . fill in the missing names: Harper, McGinnigle and . . . . ; Kerr, ...

and Shaw; Ritchie, Dunn, ... , ... and Walker.

142 Which one of those famous players was manager of the club in the "golden era" of the early 1950s?

143 Who was the luckless Hibs defender who diverted a shot past his own goalkeeper for the only goal of the 1958 Scottish Cup final?

144 Can you name the famous "whistler" with the initials "JM" who refereed that Clyde v Hibs final in 1958?

145 Jim McArthur saved an extra-time penalty in the 2nd replay of the 1979 Scottish Cup final. Can you name the Rangers player who missed the spot kick?

146 Can you name the player who scored Rangers' third and match-winning goal in that 1979 2nd replay?

147 Can you name the "Giant Killers" beaten 1-0 by Hibs in a February 1967 Scottish Cup tie in front of a near-30,000 crowd?

148 Hibernian beat Glasgow Rangers in the 1943/44 Scottish Southern League Cup final. What was the margin of Hibs' victory?

149 Where were Hibs knocked out of the Scottish Cup in season 1986/87 and what was the match result?

150 Which team did Hibs beat 2-1 in a March 1965 Scottish Cup tie and what was the significance of that result?

151 Which team beat Hibernian 2-1 in the 1947 Scottish Cup final, and who scored our goal in the first minute of the match?

152 The fellow who grabbed the winner in that 1947 final was a South African who had guested for Hibs during the war. Can you name him?

153 The man who refereed that 1947 final became a famous Pittodrie scout. Can you name him?

154 "Extra! Extra! Sweet Revenge for Hibs". To which match did that *Sunday Express* headline refer in August 1972?

155 Can you name the two players who scored the extra-time Cup-clinching goals in that 1972 Hampden final?

156 What was the score in the final of the same competition a year later, and who scored the goal which floored Celtic on this occasion?

157 Which Scottish club did Hibs meet in the first round of the 1977/78 Anglo-Scottish Cup, and what were the home and away scores?

158 Which Lancashire side did Hibs meet in the 2nd round, and what were the home and away scores in that tie?

159 Which team eliminated Hibernian from the competition at the semi-final stage, and what were the home and away scores?

160 Who did Hibs meet in the first round of the Coronation Cup at Ibrox in May 1953 and what was the outcome of that match?

161 Who were Hibernian's opponents in the Coronation Cup semi-final and what was the match result?

162 Who were Hibs' opponents in the Hampden final and what was the result of that match?

163 Can you name the player who scored a hat-trick v Dundee at Easter Road in a March 1974 Scottish Cup tie which went to a replay?

164 Can you name the goalscorers for Hibs when Aberdeen were beaten 2-1 in the 1979 Scottish Cup semi at Hampden?

165 Against which club did Hibs play a Scottish Cup away tie at Easter Road in February 1979 and what was the match result?

166 When and on what occasion did Hibs play in front of a crowd of 143,570?

167 Aberdeen won the 1947 Scottish Cup final, but Hibs got revenge in the same competition the following season . . . What was the result, and can you supply details of the amazing sequence of misfortunes which Hibernian overcame to win the tie?

168 Can you name the Norwegian player who scored both Hibs' goals in a 2-0 League Cup quarter-final 2nd leg victory over Morton at Easter Road in November 1978?

169 Which team did Hibs beat 6-0 in the first round of the 1985/86 Skol Cup, and who scored a hat-trick in that match?

170 What was the scoreline when Motherwell visited Edinburgh in the next round, and who was the hat-trick hero on this occasion?

171 Who were Hibs' quarter-final opponents and what was the match result?

172 Hibs beat Rangers 2-0 in the semi-final 1st leg at Easter Road. Which player scored on his club debut?

173 What was the match result in the final of that 1985/86 Skol Cup competition?

174 This club won the Scottish Cup for the first time in 1939 after beating Hibs 1-0 in a Tynecastle semi-final. Who are they?

175 What was unusual about Hibernian's 2-1 victory over Motherwell in the 1947 Scottish Cup semi-final?

176 What was the score when Hibs and Rangers clashed in the 1941 Summer Cup final?

177 Hibs and Rangers met again in the same final the following year. Who won the trophy, and how?

178 Where did Hibernian win the Summer Cup in September 1964 and what was the match result?

179 Can you name the player who scored a hat-trick for the club in a major final and ended up on the losing side?

180 Hibs beat Rangers 3-2 before a 100,000-plus crowd in a 1951 Scottish Cup tie at Ibrox. Who scored the winning goal for Hibernian?

181 Can you name the Hibs goalscorers when Rangers were beaten 2-1 in a 1958 Scottish Cup semi-final replay?

182 Which club did Hibs beat 1-0 in the 2nd round of the Skol Cup on 20 August 1986, and who scored?

183 Seven days later Hibs won by the same scoreline in the next round of the competition. Can you name the opponents and the goalscorer on this occasion?

184 This player scored the only goal of a January 1980 Scottish Cup tie on an old stomping-ground of his against opponents who had borrowed the venue and for whom he was later to play. Can you name him?

185 Which team did Hibs beat 2-0 in August 1963 to win a League Cup section and qualify for the last eight for the first time in ten years?

186 Hibs clinched their League Cup section in August 1974 with a last-minute winner in a 1-0 victory over Rangers at Ibrox. Who scored?

187 Hibs won the Drybrough Cup in 1972. Which side did they beat in the first round of the competition?

188 Can you name the inside-forward who scored a 1957 Scottish Cup-winning goal for Falkirk while still on Hibs' books?

189 Who was the only player to represent the club in both the 1972 Scottish Cup final v Celtic and the 1979 final v Rangers?

190 Hibs played twelve League Cup matches between August 1972 and the December final. Which was the only team to beat them?

191 Which famous club did Hibs beat 4-2 at Easter Road in the first of those twelve matches?

192 Having won the section, which club were defeated 5-2 in the 2nd round 1st leg, and who scored a hat-trick in that match?

193 What were the match results in both legs of the 3rd round tie v Airdrie?

194 Can you name the player who scored a hat-trick at Broomfield?

195 Hibs beat Rangers 1-0 in the semi. Whose power-packed winner floored the "Light Blues"?

196 It was Hibs 2 Celtic 1 in the final. Which two players scored for Hibernian and, just for the record, who notched the Celtic goal?

197 After that great win, which legendary Hibee said: "The fans should forget the old 'Famous Five' and start talking about the new 'Famous Eleven'"?

198 Can you name the goalscorer, the year and the occasion?

199 What was the result of the match?

NICKNAMES (I)

Do you know the nicknames of the following ex-Hibs players? . . . Additional clues in brackets where felt required.

200 Bobby Johnstone . . . Had a knack for "stealing" goals.

201 Ally Brazil . . . TV "soap" character from *Crossroads*.

202 Tony Higgins . . . A likeable TV monster.

203 Jim McArthur . . . A comical character.

204 Mike McDonald . . . Rolling up for pre-season training a little overweight, Mike's team-mates named him after an Italian ex-world heavyweight boxing champ.

205 Johnny Hamilton . . . Sounds like a small boat.

206 Gordon Smith . . . Too easy?

207 Jimmy Dunn (1920's international star) . . . Glaswegian word for lemonade.
208 Ally MacLeod (1970's version) . . . Nickname derives from a "big gun" American TV detective.
209 Bobby Baxter (1940's player) . . . Royalty in an Edinburgh district?

PICTURE QUIZ

210 Against which two clubs did big Willie Irvine score hat-tricks in August and November 1983?

211 Capped v Ireland in 1902, this great Hibee became the club's
manager and one of the most influential figures in the history
of Hibernian.

212 Name the 1950's Hibernian goalkeeper whose son played 30 times for Scotland between 1974 and 1981.

213 Can you recall the names of the two footballing brothers who were Scottish internationalists and who both played for Hibs in the 1960s?

214 Willie Ormond's brother played for Airdrie and Dundee United. Do you know his Christian name?

215 A "sizzling" Hibs forward in the 1950s, this fellow's son, Derek, has played for several Scottish clubs in the 1980s. Can you name him?

216 Which famous post-Second World War captain is directly related to Michael Whelehan who, in 1875, was the club's first ever "skipper"?

217 Name the Easter Road player of the 1980s whose dad joined Hibs from Celtic in November 1968.

218 Neil Orr's late father, Tommy, played twice for Scotland and spent 16 years attached to only one senior club. Can you name the club?

219 Name the Hibernian full-back who played eight times for Scotland between 1946 and 1948 and whose brother, Jock, was also an internationalist.

220 Identify the Hibs goalie from the early 1960s whose father, Jimmy, was a Rangers and Scotland star in the 1930s.

221 And still on goalies, Andy Goram's dad kept goal for the club in the 1950s. What is his first name?

222 These footballing brothers were both Hibernian centre-forwards in the early 1960s.

223 This father and son both played centre-half for the club . . . dad in the 1950s and his lad in the late 1970s and early 1980s.

224 Can you name two brothers, one a winger/defender and the other a coach, who were attached to Hibernian around the late 1970s and early 1980s?

225 The son of a German father who played for Borussia Münchengladbach, this full-back was capped v Germany in 1974.

226 This inside-forward played for the club just before the war. His son was named after him and has starred for Dumbarton, Celtic, Borussia Dortmund and Scotland. What's the name?

227 Willie was the Celtic boss in the 1920s while brother Alex managed Hibs. What's the surname?

228 What is the relationship between Hibs Chairman David Duff and Managing Director Jim Gray?

229 Which member of the current Hibernian staff has a brother who manages an English First Division club?

230 This Hibs manager once played for Falkirk and the Scottish League. His brother, also a manager, played in the Preston team which won the FA Cup in 1938.

PICTURE QUIZ

231 One for the youngsters . . . Who is this 1980's striker?

232 Can you name the two Premier League clubs for which he played before joining Hibs in 1985?

233 To which club did Hibernian transfer this player in October 1987?

... And dad will remember Johnny McLeod!

234 Apart from Hibs, with which two clubs were Johnny McLeod and Joe Baker team-mates?

235 How many times did Johnny play for Scotland?

236 Against which country did he make his international debut?

237 He played well in that match . . . so why should he, perhaps, wish to forget the occasion?

238 Against which club did he score a hat-trick in a December 1959 League fixture?

239 What was the result of that match?

240 . . . And the ladies will like the look of this handsome chap photographed in 1960. Who is he?

Any grandad who loves you will know about Bobby Combe!

241 In which year did Bobby join Hibernian?

242 Against which club did he score four goals in September of the same year?

243 What was the result of the above match?

244 How many times did Bobby play for Scotland at full international level?

245 Against which country did he make his international debut?

246 For which other senior clubs did he play?

247 He did, however, manage another club . . . which one?

248 In which year did Hibernian become the first Scottish side to install undersoil heating?

249 Who was Hibs' first official substitute in a competitive match, and who were the opponents?

250 Before Alex Miller, who was the last manager who had never been afforded the privilege of wearing the famous green and white jersey of Hibernian?

251 Can you name eight post-war Hibernian managers who did have the honour of playing for the club?

252 A great character, this former Easter Road star is now Secretary of the Scottish Professional Footballers' Association.

253 This 1960's centre-forward became a TV sports presenter with BBC Scotland and a high-ranking official with the Independent Broadcasting Authority.

254 Another 1960's forward, this speed merchant became a professional sprint champion.

255 Can you name the two post-war Hibernian goalkeepers who became directors of the club?

256 Can you name a rival club of the 1870s who shared the same name as a German city and an Edinburgh street?

257 Which player, in season 1959/60, scored Hibs' individual record number of League goals in a season?

258 Can you name three Hibernian "skippers" who became managers of Aberdeen?

259 . . . And a former Hibs captain who spent almost two years in the "Granite City" as Alex Ferguson's assistant?

260 What was the score when Dunfermline played Hibs in a September 1966 League match?

261 In which year did Hibs become the first Scottish side to have a sponsor's name on their shirts?

262 Can you name the sponsor?

263 Who was the last player to score a hat-trick for the Hibees at Celtic Park and what was the match result?

264 Which Scottish League club had been fortunate enough to avoid meeting Hibernian in any competition up to the end of season 1987/88?

265 Which country has a League club called Hibernians?

266 Hibs and the "Bully Wee" have had some great tussles over the years . . . who are they?

267 Where were Hibs touring in the late 1960s when accused in the United Nations of being paratroops in disguise?

268 Can you name the wholehearted Hibee who is currently the club's longest- serving player?

269 What is Hibernian's highest win in the Premier League, and who were the luckless opponents?

270 In which year did Hibernian first wear those now famous green shirts with white sleeves?

271 Why did Hibs and Stenhousemuir stage a match at Ochilview on 7 November 1984?

272 Can you name the Hibernian manager who won an FA Cup winner's medal with Manchester City in 1956?

273 Which ex-Hib was also a member of City's 1956 Cup-winning side?

274 From which foreign club did goalkeeper Jim Herriot join Hibs in August 1971?

275 Which player scored six hat-tricks for Hibs in season 1972/73?

276 Which famous athlete made his first public appearance at Easter Road after winning an Olympic gold medal?

277 What was the attendance at the 1958 Clyde v Hibs Scottish Cup final? A: 78,690   B: 95,123   C: 62,400

278 Which two players appeared for Hibs in both the 1947 and 1958 Scottish Cup finals?

279 Which team did Hibs thrash 9-2 in the League Cup on 28 August 1976?

280 What unusual distinction did defender Alan Sneddon achieve in season 1980/81?

281 Hibs bought big Neil Martin from the "Doonhamers" in July 1963 . . . who are they?

282 Gordon Smith starred for Hibs, Hearts and Dundee, but for which Irish club did he play?

283 Name the 1970's Hibs forward who played for both Dundee clubs as well as Hibs and Hearts.

284 Following an unfortunate incident at Berwick in season

1980/81, which player was mentioned in the *Guinness Book of Records*?

285 This football legend guested for Hibernian during the war and was knighted in 1968 for his services to football.

286 Who scored Hibs' goals when Real Madrid lost to Scottish opposition for the first time at Easter Road in 1964?

287 Can you name a famous "Saint" who scored a 1959 hat-trick against Hibs at Easter Road in a record two-and-a-half minutes?

288 One of football's top trainer/physios, from which club did Tom McNiven join Hibernian in 1963?

289 Which significant statement with regard to the ground did the Hibernian directors announce to the press in August 1981?

290 Which Hibs player was the Premier League's top marksman in season 1985/86 and how many goals did he score?

291 What was the title of the Hibs book published in 1975 and written by Gerry Docherty and Phil Thomson?

292 Can you name the author of the recent and excellent book which traces the history of the club and is entitled *The Hibees*?

293 Which well-known sports journalist wrote *Hibernian Greats*, published in 1987?

294 Who said Jimmy O'Rourke had "Hibernian stitched across his chest"?

295 Internationalists Johnny McLeod and Willie Hamilton shared the same middle name . . . what is it? (Clue: This Celtic right-half was a "Lisbon Lion".)

296 In which season did Hibs establish a record by drawing half of their League fixtures?

297 Can you name the eminent surgeon who was a member of the Hibernian board in the 1960s and 1970s?

298 Between 19 December 1987 and 16 January 1988 Hibs failed to score in five Premier League outings. Who ended the goal famine at Cappielow on 23 January?

299 Hibs must have felt like fools when this Irish team beat them on 1 April 1957, score 2-1. (Clue: Club name has connection with an alcoholic drink.)

300 Which former Hibernian manager once played for Queen's Park and Clyde?

301 Jock Stein became manager of the club in the spring of 1964. Who were the opposition in his first match and what was the result?

302 Stein left Easter Road in March 1965. Who succeeded him as manager?

303 Which player headed Hibs' seventh goal in the 1973 demolition of Hearts at Tynecastle?

304 Why was the 1968/69 Celtic v Hibs League Cup final played in the spring of 1969 and not in the autumn of 1968 as planned?

305 Why did Hibernian's fans wish the above game had never been played?

306 To which club was forward, Alex McGhee, transferred in 1979?

307 For which two clubs did ex-Hibee Colin Harris play in season 1987/88?

308 Pictured in the 1950s, this young Third Lanark player became a Hibs captain in the 1960s. Can you name him?

309 From which Lancashire club did he join Hibs?

310 In which season was he Hibernian's only ever-present player?

311 How many of this 1969 line-up do you recognise?

312 Which player was an ex-Rangers, Everton and Scotland star?

313 Who joined Hibs from Third Lanark in 1963?

314 Which five players represented Motherwell at some stage in their career?

315 Which of these Hibs stars were on Hearts' books during their playing career?

316 Can you name the three players who also played for Morton?

317 Which players became managers, and which clubs did they manage?

318 Pictured in 1970, these youthful "Buddies" became great
"Hibees". Can you name them?

319 Do the youngsters know who the "Buddies" are and in which
town they play?

Name the opponents which Hibernian played on the following grounds in both competitive and friendly matches since the war.

320 Boothferry Park.
321 Estadio Ramon Sanchez Pizjuan.
322 Shielfield Park.
323 Filbert Street.
324 Gayfield.
325 Deepdale.
326 Boundary Park.
327 Glebe Park.
328 Gran Estadio.
329 Ashton Gate.
330 Recreation Park.
331 Empire Games Stadium.
332 Annfield.
333 Cathkin Park.
334 Ayresome Park.
335 Boroughbriggs.
336 Stadio Comunale.
337 Volksparkstadion.
338 Central Park.
339 Stadio Fuorigrotta.
340 St James's Park.
341 Bezigrad Stadium.
342 Springfield Park.
343 Estadio das Antas.
344 Anfield.
345 Bramall Lane.
346 Baseball Ground.
347 Station Park.
348 Belle Vue Ground.
349 Blundell Park.
350 Bootham Crescent.
351 Ewood Park.
352 Firs Park.
353 Gigg Lane.

354 Leeds Road.
355 Maine Road.
356 Ochilview.
357 Somerset Park.

PICTURE QUIZ

358 Can you recognise these 1980's Hibees who've been caught with their pants down?

359 Edinburgh honours the 1972 League Cup winners . . .
which player scored most goals in the competition?

360 Hibs played a total of 12 matches. How many goals did they
score? Was it – *A*: 26   *B*: 32   *C*: 34?

361 An old pals' act . . . why were manager Pat Stanton and John
Blackley smiling in July 1983?

362 Can you spot the recent signings photographed in July 1969?

Crossword-style clues. Additional clues in brackets where felt necessary.

363 There was once a car factory here. (1940's centre-forward).

364 He only made only sub appearance in 1985, so it could be difficult to "come to grips" with this player who has the same name as a famous wrestler.

365 Sounds as if he's losing his hair . . . but not quite! (1970's defender).

366 Just for the *Record* this candid fellow was a Hibernian full-back in the early 1960s.

367 . . . And, sharing the name of a *Record* colleague, this football "scribe" was signed from St Mirren in June 1970.

368 A very famous band leader.

369 These two Hibernian players were always in the Highland soup (1940's player and 1950's/1960's player).

370 One of the smallest birds in Britain (1950's goalkeeper).

371 Another bird which looks like a swallow.

372 . . . And a big bird in every sense!

373 This 1980's star has the same surname as a famous Celt and a beautiful actress?

374 A cunning customer! (1950's inside-forward).

375 These chaps would quickly track down the answer to the previous question. (1960's/1970's player and 1980's player).

376 You could almost sing his praises at Christmas! (1970's player).

377 Nearly half of a famous Edinburgh university! (The other half was a former boxing champ.)

378 Close to where the kids often play football? (1960's defender).

379 Sounds like a Welsh rugby player . . . but Hibs signed this Englishman from Rotherham in 1988!

380 Another Hibee with a Welsh name . . . this time a 1960's/1970's defender!

381 Signed from Leicester City in the 1980s, this "boyo" would be sure of a warm welcome in the Valleys!

382 With a name like that this chap should have played rugby for a Lanarkshire town! (Hibs' top league scorer in season 1900-01).

383 Meanwhile this 1980's twosome could give you the "Willies" in an Ayrshire town!

384 This relation could have been a "kissin' " or a "country" one in the 1960s!

385 This 1950's forward, who played for both Hibs and Hearts, has the same surname as a much publicised opposition manager.

386 Capped against Ireland in 1900, this forward had the same surname as a Labour Prime Minister!

387 He was a 1980's transfer to Notts Forest . . . not a Chinese paddy field!

388 A large town in Lancashire! (1950's/1960's forward).

389 Sharing *both* his Christian and surnames with a famous snooker player, this full-back was an expert penalty 'potter' in the 1960s!

390 Double "Scotch" (1950's/1960's defender and 1980's midfield player).

391 You'll find lots of animals here! (1940's goalkeeper).

392 Transferred to Motherwell in 1948 . . . it sounds as if this fellow had a pain in the temple!

393 This 1980's defender has the same surname as he of *Scotch and Wry* fame!

394 . . . And this 1970's defender shared his first name with the same comedian!

395 This fair-haired 1970's defender shared his surname with a famous Border knitwear firm!

396 Hibs' top League goalscorer in season 1917/18, this fellow had the same name as a former Hibernian goalkeeper and an Aberdeen and Scotland star!

397 This 1960's forward had the same surname as a 1960's manager!

398 It's great to score v Rangers as Big Tony Higgins demonstrates in December 1979. When and where did this genial giant score another goal against the "Light Blues" in 1979?

399 When and in what competition did Tony score a dramatic extra-time winner against Rangers in a 1970's semi-final?

400 For which other senior clubs did this great character play?

401 This fresh-faced Scottish Schoolboy internationalist joined Hibs in 1962 . . . who is he?

402 For which famous Edinburgh school did he play?

403 How many hat-tricks did he score for Hibs in competitive matches . . . was it: *A*: 10 *B*: 12 *C*: 6?

404 After 12 years' marvellous service, to which club was he transferred in August 1974?

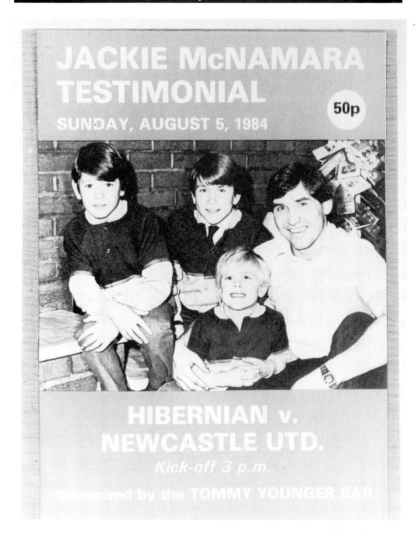

405 Where and when did Jackie make his Hibernian debut?

406 Can you name the opposition when Jackie made a scoring appearance for the Scottish League in 1980?

407 What was the scoreline when this fine Hibs servant was honoured with a testimonial match v Newcastle United?

408 From which club did Hibs sign George Best in November 1979?

409 How much did Hibernian pay for his transfer? Was it: *A*: £75,000   *B*: £42,500   *C*: £50,000?

410 What age was Best when he joined Hibs?

411 Who were Hib's opponents when George made his home debut, and what was the match result?

412 Who were Hibernian's first-ever opponents in European competition and what were the home and away scores in that tie?

413 Who was the first Hibs player to score a hat-trick in European competition, and can you name the opponents?

414 "Eleven heroes gave Scottish football its greatest ever boost" . . . to what event was the *Daily Record* referring in December 1960?

415 Who were the Hibernian goalscorers on that auspicious occasion?

416 Can you name two famous Hungarian-born forwards who opposed Hibs in that match?

417 Can you recall the 2nd leg score and name the Hibs player who scored a dramatic winner from the penalty spot?

418 Why was the evening of 23 October 1962 wonderful, wonderful for Morris Stevenson?

419 What were the home and away scores in that tie?

420 "Hibs wrote the greatest chapter in their long and glorious history" . . . to what was the *Daily Record* referring in November 1967?

421 What was the significance of that scoreline?

422 Which famous Brazilian player had scored against Hibs in the 1st leg match of that tie?

423 Can you name the world-renowned Italian goalkeeper who will certainly want to forget his first visit to Easter Road?

424 The same 'keeper was a much happier fellow when he returned to the stadium in October 1974. Why?

425 Who scored Hibs' goal in a 1-0 1st leg Fairs Cup victory over Utrecht in Holland in 1962?

426 Can you recall the score and scorers in the 2nd leg v Utrecht and name the player who made his first-team debut in that match when aged only sixteen?

427 Which French side beat Hibs in the semi-final of the European Cup in 1956 and what was the aggregate score?

428 Can you name the famous forward who played for the Frenchmen and who went on to win three European Cup winner's medals with Real Madrid?

429 Can you name the two other French clubs which Hibs have met in European competition?

430 Which Swiss club scratched from the 1960/61 Fairs Cup tournament and presented Hibs with a walk-over?

431 Against which Portuguese club did Jim O'Rourke score a Cup Winner's Cup hat-trick in September 1972?

432 Can you recall the result in the away leg of that tie, and in what colours Hibernian played in Portugal?

433 What was the result of the 2nd leg match when wee Jimmy scored that marvellous hat-trick on 27 September 1972?

434 What was the half-time score in that match?

435 Can you name the former England internationalist who was manager of the Portuguese club?

436 Against which side did Hibernian achieve their highest aggregate score in Europe?

437 Hibs recorded their biggest win against the same opponents . . . what was the score?

438 Against which European club did Hibs play an *away* match at Partick Thistle's Firhill ground, and why?

439 What were the results in both legs of that 1955-56 European Cup tie, and which Hibs player scored from the penalty spot on each occasion?

440 Can you name the East Europeans beaten 7-1 at Easter Road in a 1972/73 Cup Winners Cup tie, and which player scored a hat-trick in that match?

441 Can you name the Hibernian player who scored a hat-trick in the next round of the same competition, and against whom?

442 What were the home and away scores in that tie?

443 Who were the opponents on the only occasion on which the club were eliminated due to the away goals rule?

444 What were the scores in both legs, and can you name the famous striker who scored the crucial 2nd leg goal?

445 Who scored a hat-trick for Hibs in a 6-0 Fairs Cup win over Malmøe of Sweden at Easter Road on 16 September 1970?

446 Can you name the first Portuguese side to visit Easter Road in European competition and give the scores in both legs?

447 Who scored an Easter Road double against those Portuguese visitors. In the 1961-62 Fairs Cup competition?

448 Which French side did Hibernian oust 1-0 on aggregate in the 1976/77 UEFA Cup, and who scored the vital Easter Road winner?

449 Can you name the three clubs which Hibs have met twice in European competition?

450 Which club knocked Hibs out at the semi-final stage of the 1960/61 Fairs Cup tournament?

451 What were the scores in both legs of the 1970/71 Fairs Cup tie against Portugal's Vitoria Guimares?

452 Who scored the all-important goal in Portugal?

453 Which player scored Hibernian's 100th goal in European competition?

454 Hibs and Leeds United drew 1-1 in a January 1968 Fairs Cup 2nd leg match. Whose late goal knocked Hibs out of the competition?

455 Who missed a crucial penalty when the Yorkshire side revisited Easter Road for a November 1973 UEFA Cup tie?

456 What had been the aggregate score after 210 minutes' play?

457 Can you recall the three other occasions on which Hibs failed to score on aggregate in normal time?

458 Which famous Welshman scored Liverpool's goal in the "Reds'" 1-0 victory over Hibs at Easter Road on 9 December 1970?

459 Can you give the scores in both legs when Hibs and Liverpool clashed again in the 1975/76 UEFA Cup?

460 Who scored a hat-trick for Liverpool in the second match?

461 Which player scored for Hibernian at Anfield?

462 Can you name Hibernian's only Icelandic opponents in European competition?

463 Hibs beat the Icelanders 2-0 at Easter Road. Who scored the home side's goals?

464 Which Swedish side did Hibs beat 3-2 on aggregate in the 1978/79 UEFA Cup competition?

465 Which two Hibernian players share the honour of having scored most goals for the club in Europe?

466 Which Yugoslav team did Hibs eliminate from the 1968/69 Fairs Cup?

467 Hibs beat the Slavs 2-1 at Easter Road. Which player scored both of the home side's goals, and how?

468 Which players scored Hibs' goals in the 3-0 Fairs Cup victory over Porto at Easter Road on 20 September 1967?

469 Hibs were beaten 3-1 by Porto in Portugal. Who scored the all-important goal?

470 Can you name the Hibs goalkeeper pitched into the side which were beaten 4-0 by Red Star Belgrade in a 1961 Fairs Cup tie played in Yugoslavia?

471 Why was regular goalkeeper, Ronnie Simpson, unable to play?

472 Which player scored a last-minute goal v Valencia at Easter Road on 8 September 1965, and what was the result of that Fairs Cup 1st leg match?

473 What was the match result when Hibs travelled to Spain for the 2nd leg?

474 Who won the deciding match and where was it played?

475 Who were Hibs' last opponents in European competition, and can you recall the scores in both legs of the tie?

476 High Steppin' Hibees . . . can you recognise this happy late 1940's line-up?

477 Step it up lads . . . can you name the first six personalities "enjoying" a training session on the old terracing in the late 1950s?

478 This "Galloping Major" from Hungary visited Easter Road on 7 October 1964.

479 Wee "Dixie" scored a hat-trick against Hibs in the 1972 Scottish Cup final . . . what's his real name?

480 Hibs signed Ally MacLeod from these "Saints" in 1974.

481 The other Ally McLeod has managed those "Honest Men" three times.

482 John Blackley was transferred to "The Magpies" in October 1977 . . . who are they?

483 Hibs and "The Swans" drew 1-1 in an August 1980 friendly. Name the opponents.

484 This famous player was the "Darlin' " of the fans before the turn of the century.

485 These lucky "Diamonds" beat Hibs 2-0 in the 1924 Scottish Cup final.

486 Name the unhappy opposition when the "Hibees" beat the "Hi-Hi" 8-4 in December 1960.

487 Hibs stung these "Wasps" eleven times on 22 September 1965.

488 Hibs beat "The Loons" 8-1 in a 1971 Scottish Cup tie. Who are they?

489 Can you name the "Warriors" whom Hibs trounced 8-1 in a 1953 Scottish Cup tie?

490 These "Gable Endies" shocked Hibernian in the 1975/76 League Cup competition.

491 "The Toffees" were welcome visitors in 1962.

492 Bolton Wanderers and Hibs are old rivals . . . what's the Lancashire club's nickname?

493 Hibs signed Roy Barry from these "Eagles" in 1975.

494 Who are the opponents when the "Hibees" take a trip to "Paradise"?

495 Hibs beat these "Blues" 2-0 at St Andrews in 1968.

496 You can collect your kippers and smokies when Hibernian next visit "The Red Lichties".

497 Joe Tortolano left these "Throstles" to become a Hibee in 1985.

498 This "Juke Box" became a "Pensioner" in the mid-1980s . . . player and club please?
499 These "Zebras" from Turin faced Hibs in a 1970's European tie.
500 A 1980's Hibee, "Toby" once scored the winner in a Scottish Cup final.
501 "The Terriers" beat Hibernian 3-2 in March 1956 . . . who are they?
502 Hibs beat "The Tigers" 3-2 in February 1953 . . . what is their name?

PICTURE QUIZ

503 Which marvellous record are these 1970's Hibees recording?
504 None of these songsters represented any real threat to Frank Sinatra, but can you name them?
505 Who is the fellow conducting this unlikely choir?

506 Can you recognise this 1960's player?

TRANSFERS

507 From which club did Hibs sign goalkeeper Mike McDonald in January 1976?

508 Which Hibernian player was involved in the first six-figure transfer fee between Scottish sides?

509 Eddie May joined Hibs in 1985 on a free transfer from –
A: Aberdeen   *B*: St Mirren   *C*: Dundee United.

510 Who was signed from Everton in January 1974 for £120,000, a then record fee paid by a Scottish club?

511 Can you name the Danish defender signed from Morton in 1966-67 season?

512 This Hibernian goalkeeper guested for Rangers during the war.

513 Hibs paid Blackpool £26,000 for this inside-forward in October 1963.

514 This ex-Motherwell and Scotland player came to Easter Road from Detroit Cougars, USA, during season 1968/69.

515 Which two players joined Hibs in a 1976 swop deal which took Iain Munro to Ibrox?

516 Beith-born, this stylish right-half won four Scottish Cup winner's medals with Celtic before joining Hibs in 1934.

517 Which centre-forward was transferred to Clyde for a £10,000 fee in December 1948?

518 How much did Hibs pay Aberdeen for the transfer of Steve Cowan in the summer of 1985?

519 From which Highland League club did Hibernian sign Des Bremner in November 1972?

520 This international wingman became a "Gunner" in June 1961. (Player and club please).

521 This prolific scorer was sent to Coventry via Sunderland in October 1965.

522 This goalkeeper took the "Road and the Miles" to Dundee in July 1971.

523 From which club did Hibs sign Gordon Durie in 1984?

524 For which ex-Morton player did Hibernian pay Middlesbrough £80,000 in 1982?

525 Colin Harris arrived at Easter Road and this striker joined Dundee in a 1985 swop deal.

526 To which club did Hibs transfer Joe McBride in December 1970?

527 For which inside-forward did Leicester City pay Hibernian £24,000 in January 1962?

528 This Linfield player signed for Hibs in the summer of 1986 while in Albuquerque, USA, with the Irish World Cup squad.

529 Joining Hibs from Armadale Thistle in 1957, this powerfully built full-back spent seven years at Easter Road before signing for Wrexham.

530 To which club did Hibernian pay £100,000 for the transfer of Neil Orr in August 1987?

531 For which forward did Hibs pay Clyde £10,000 in February 1947?

532 What was the significance of the above transfer?

533 This Turnbull joined Hibs from Dundee in 1981 . . . what was his first name?

534 To which club did Hibs pay £65,000 for Gordon Chisholm in 1985?

535 How much did Hibs pay Partick Thistle for the transfer of Alan Rough in November 1982?

536 Manager Willie Ormond signed this Scottish internationalist for St Johnstone in the late 1960s and for Hibs in 1980.

537 This inside-forward/wing-half won seven caps with Rangers and joined Hibs in October 1960 for £5,000.

538 A member of St Mirren's 1959 Scottish Cup-winning side, this half-back was bought from Liverpool in 1962.

539 From which club did Hibs sign defender Graham Mitchell in December 1986?

540 This striker came to Easter Road from Cowdenbeath in February 1964.

541 In 1962 Hibs signed inside-forward Johnny Byrne from – A: Bury   B: Sheffield United   C: Tranmere Rovers.

542 Capped twice for Scotland, this long-serving defender was signed from Merchiston Thistle in 1949 and transferred to Raith Rovers in September 1964.

543 Which forward joined Hibernian in September 1979 in a part-exchange deal which took Des Bremner to Aston Villa?

544 With which ex-team-mate did Bremner renew his acquaintance at Villa Park?

545 This goalkeeper won six caps with Celtic and came to Easter Road from Clyde in January 1954.

546 From which club did Hibs sign inside-forward Morris Stevenson in 1962?

547 To which club did Hibernian transfer goalkeeper Lawrie Leslie for £4,475 in November 1959?

548 This goalie arrived at Easter Road from Cowdenbeath on 23 October 1972.

549 To which club did Hibs transfer international goalkeeper Willie Harper in November 1925?

550 What was the significance of Harper's transfer?

551 Manchester City paid £17,500 for the transfer of this centre-half in July 1960.

552 Which two Dundee United players became Hibees in 1986 following a £150,000 deal?

553 From which club did Gerry Baker join Hibs in 1961 and to whom was he transferred in 1963?

554 Which goalkeeper left Easter Road for St Mirren in July 1973?

555 From which club did Hibernian sign Alan Gordon on 20 January 1972?

556 Hibs signed this striker from Dundee in a November 1977 exchange deal involving Erich Schaedler.

557 From which club had Schaedler joined Hibernian in November 1969?

558 Which club did Alex Edwards join on leaving Easter Road in 1979?

559 To which club was Ally Scott transferred in 1978?

560 To which club was Sammy Baird transferred in November 1962?

561 Which club did Alex Scott join on leaving Hibs in 1970?

562 Jim Scott was transferred to Newcastle in 1967, but for which other English club did he play?

563 To which club was defender Rab Kilgour transferred in 1980?

564 From which club did Gary Murray join Hibernian in 1980?

565 John Brogan joined Hibs in 1984 . . . from whom?

566 To which club was Colin Campbell transferred in 1980?

567 From which club was Gerry O'Brien signed in 1978?

568 Capped twice while with Kilmarnock, this centre-half joined
Hibs in April 1963. Who is he?

569 From which club did Tommy Younger join Hibs in 1948?

570 To which club was he transferred for £9,000 in June 1956?

571 For which other clubs did big Tommy play?

572 How many times did he play for Scotland in full international matches?

573 In what capacity did he return to Easter Road in October 1969?

574 At the time of his death in January 1984, what high office did Tommy Younger hold in Scottish football?

575 Pictured in 1956, this young player became a Hibee 12 years later. Who is he?

576 Which team's colours is he wearing in the photograph? (Clue: A well-known Junior club with a famous Scottish brigand included in its name).

577 Can you identify this 1960's centre-half?
578 To which club was he transferred in season 1964/65?

579 Against which club and in what competition did Iain make a scoring home debut after joining Hibs from St Mirren in 1973?

580 Against which club did he score a League hat-trick in March 1975?

581 How many times did he play for Scotland at full international level while a St Mirren player?

582 From which club did Iain Munro rejoin Hibernian in 1985?

583 In season 1987/88 he was Assistant Manager of which Premier League club?

584 Can you name the three former Hibernian players who became managers of Scotland's national side?

585 Who is the only English-born Easter Road player to represent Scotland at full international level while on the club payroll?

586 This famous Hibs inside-forward played in the Scottish side which hammered England 5-1 in March 1928 and became known as "The Wembley Wizards".

587 Who was the only Hibs player to be capped for Wales while on the Easter Road payroll?

588 A Scots Guards heavyweight boxing champion, this Hibee protected the Scottish goal during Wembley's first-ever international in April 1924.

589 Who is the only other goalkeeper to represent Scotland at Wembley while on Hibernian's books?

590 Can you name five other Hibs goalkeepers who played for Scotland at Wembley although not Hibernian players at the time?

591 Apart from "Roughie", who was the last Hibs player to appear for Scotland at Wembley?

592 Against which country did young John Collins make a scoring international debut in February 1988?

593 Apart from Collins, who was the last Hibs player to score for Scotland in a full international match?

594 This Hibee came on as a substitute against Switzerland at Hampden in 1976 to win his only full cap.

595 Against which country did Jim Scott win his only full international honour in May 1966?

596 Which Hibs player collected the last of his full caps against Sweden at Hampden in 1977?

597 Capped v Wales in 1923 and against Ireland in 1928, this famous winger was a £4,000 transfer to Everton in August 1928.

598 From a Hibernian viewpoint why were the 1948 internationals against Belgium and Switzerland memorable?

599 Joe Baker was an England player, but for which country did his brother Gerry play at international level?

600 Capped four times with Hibs and Manchester City in the early 1900s, this winger has the same name as a 1970's centre-half.

601 This centre-half was only five feet four inches tall, yet he was capped v Wales in 1896 when with Hibs and v Wales in 1900 when with Rangers.

602 Can you name the Hibernian midfielder with the initials "LM" who played for Scotland's under-21s against Czechoslovakia in 1977?

603 Which over-age ex-Hibs player captained the Scots in that under-21 match versus the Czechs?

604 Against which two countries did Neil Martin play for Scotland in 1965 while a Hibernian player?

605 Can you name the Hibernian forward who played for Eire v Switzerland and France in 1937 and for Northern Ireland v Wales in 1938?

606 Can you name the once-capped Easter Road defender who played for the Republic of Ireland v Luxembourg in 1954?

607 Who were the two Northern Ireland internationalists signed from Linfield in December 1935?

608 Can you name the Hibs full-back who scored v. Wales in October 1948 on his only full international appearance for Scotland?

609 Which other Hibernian player made his Scotland debut in that 1948 Cardiff international?

610 Capped v Ireland in March 1909, this full-back died in the same year, aged 23, because of internal injuries sustained in a Christmas Day friendly against Partick Thistle.

611 Against which three countries did Gordon Smith score in consecutive internationals in May 1955?

612 Who were Scotland's Hampden opponents when Lawrie Reilly scored his only international hat-trick in 1952?

613 Hailed as the finest in Britain during the first decade of the 20th century, this goalkeeper was signed from Hearts and won 11 of his 13 caps while a Hibs player.

614 Can you name the three Hibs men who have played for Scotland in the final stages of the World Cup competition?

615 A Hibs goalkeeper in the 1960s, this fellow subsequently went "down under" where he was capped for Australia at full international level.

616 Can you name the Hibs forward who faced England five times in wartime internationals between October 1941 and October 1944?

617 Can you name the luckless Hibs player who made his Scotland debut in an April 1945 wartime international v England, was taken off injured in the first minute of the match and never played for his country again?

618 In 1979 Ally MacLeod played three times for Scotland's under-21s as an over-age player, once v Portugal and twice v which other country?

PICTURE QUIZ

619 Can you recognise this forward who was a prolific goalscorer in the mid-1960s?

620 This player represented Sunderland in the 1985 Milk Cup final at Wembley and Hibs in the 1985 Skol Cup final at Hampden.

621 This defender joined Hibs from Celtic in 1964, later taking part in Newcastle's successful Fairs Cities Cup campaign in 1968/69.

622 A great club servant, he scored twice for Celtic v Hibs in the 1914 Scottish Cup final replay, played for Hibernian in the 1923 and 1924 finals and later became club trainer.

623 Widely respected, Hibernian's Club Secretary has been at Easter Road since July 1971.

624 Larkhall-born, this full-back won six caps and three Championship medals before joining Ayr United in 1954.

625 Signed by Hibs in 1943, capped v Wales in 1948, this defender lost his life in a car accident.

626 An internationalist, this left-back won a Division Two Championship medal with Hibs and was transferred to Aberdeen in September 1935.

627 This 1980's Hibee has the same name as an Airdrie and Scotland star who abandoned Hearts for South America in 1950.

628 This Hibs player was transferred to Celtic in the 1960s and became Scotland's oldest international debutant.

629 Transferred to Blackpool in September 1948, this goalkeeper won ten caps and an FA Cup winner's badge while with "The Seasiders".

630 This ex-Hibernian forward scored for Leicester City v Stoke City in both legs of the 1963/64 League Cup final.

631 This ex-Hibs goalkeeper played for Stoke v Leicester in the 1st leg of that 1963/64 final.

632 One of football's great personalities, this winger played for seven senior clubs and was capped 11 times. He was a Hibs player in the late 1890s.

633 A goalkeeper with the initials "HW", he joined Hibs in 1974 and was transferred to Dunfermline in 1976.

634 A famous referee, BM was in charge of the first two 1979 Cup final matches v Rangers.

635 This midfield player came to Easter Road from Celtic in 1982 and was transferred to Blackpool in 1984.

636 WJ scored twice when Hibs visited the Highlands and drew 3-3 with BR in August 1982. (Player and club please).

637 This right-half played for the club in the 1914, 1923 and 1924 finals and joined Hearts in 1926.

638 Born in Colchester, this Englishman nicknamed "Jock" played for the Scottish League v Wales in 1953 . . . a fine centre-half!

639 This ex-Hib scored twice for Hearts when Celtic were beaten 3-1 by "The Maroons" in the 1956 Scottish Cup final.

640 Hibernian's Commercial Manager is definitely the brightest in the business.

641 A current forward, as a youngster he played at left-back when Hibs beat Airdrie 3-1 at Broomfield in a 1983 League Cup tie.

642 This former goalkeeper proved himself a prolific goalscorer for Ormiston Primrose in season 1987/88.

643 An ex-Hearts player, this wing-half captained Clyde's 1955 Scottish Cup-winning team and joined Hibs in the summer of 1956.

644 This part-time player was a Hibernian captain in the early 1980s. He also played for Morton, Clyde and Partick Thistle.

645 Hibs line-up at the start of season 1973/74 with the Drybrough and League Cups . . . how many of the players do you recognise?

646 At the time the picture was taken, who was the only player with a Scottish Cup winner's medal?

647 Two of the backroom staff were owners of the same medal. Can you name them?

648 Which of these stars once played in Australian football with Melbourne Thistle?

649 Which player came to Easter Road from Airdrie?

ENOUGH TO GIVE YOU NIGHTMARES

Hibernian have travelled along a glorious, yet sometimes bumpy, road. Here are a few of the bumps! WARNING: Don't attempt this section last thing before going to bed, or you are sure of a sleepless night!

650 The evening of 28 October 1987 was dreadful! Hibs lost 0-1 at home and had two players sent off . . . not very pleasant, but opponents and players please.

651 With a 2-0 1st leg lead, Hibernian travelled to Sweden for a 1976/77 UEFA Cup match. Who were the opponents and what was the result?

652 In which season did Hibs concede 25 goals and lose all six League Cup section games v Rangers, Dundee and Motherwell?

653 These nasty Fifers knocked Hibernian out of the "Scottish" in 1952 and 1956.

654 It will bring tears to your eyes, but what was the score when Hibs visited Tynecastle for a 1955 Scottish Cup tie?

655 Third Lanark scored 100 League goals in season 1960/61. How many did they need v Hibs in the last game of that season to hit the magic "ton" . . . and what was the match result?

656 "The Latics" beat Hibs 6-3 in the Isle of Man in the summer of 1987 . . . who are they?

657 It was a real trial for Hibs when they visited this German city in 1954 and were beaten 6-1.

658 Four first-half goals shattered Hibs when this club came to Edinburgh for an August 1987 Premier League fixture.

659 This team surprisingly won the Scottish Cup in 1938, and they shocked Hibs in a January 1984 Scottish Cup tie replay.

660 Hibs kicked off season 1956/57 with a League Cup fixture at Tynecastle . . . what was the result?

661 By November 1986 Hamilton had completed 19 Premier League fixtures without a win. What was the match result when they came to Easter Road on the 29th of that month?

662 Just to rub salt into the gaping wound, which ex-Hib scored two of the visitors' goals?

663 Alan Gordon equalised, but Hibs were hit by an avalanche of goals in the 1972 Scottish Cup final. Who were the opponents and what was the result?

664 Hibs' fans felt like digging a hole for themselves when the youngest of Scotland's clubs won 2-1 at Easter Road in a 1984 Skol Cup tie . . . who are they?

665 These "Shakers" really did bury Hibs in a February 1956 friendly.

666 These Fifers shocked Hibernian by winning 2-1 at Tynecastle in a 1949/50 League Cup semi-final.

667 Naturally an ex-Hib scored both opposition goals at Tynecastle. Can you name him?

668 John Ogilvie and Willie Ormond were both badly injured, and a depleted Hibs side lost a 1950/51 Scottish Cup semi at Tynecastle . . . who were the opponents and what was the match result?

669 The worst Christmas present in history! What was the score when Rangers played Hibs on Christmas Eve 1898?

Hibs really are a family club and the youngsters are very important . . . come on, kids, see how well you can do without dad's help!

670 Who are the happy Hibees pictured outside St Giles' Cathedral in May 1988?

671 Which player in the photograph is the Hibs captain?

672 Three of these Hibees had played in English football . . . who are they?

673 From which English clubs did they join Hibs?

674 Can you name the happy, hard-working fellow who is Secretary of the Hibs Kids' Club?

675 Who is Hibs' Assistant Manager?

Here are the nicknames of some of your Hibs heroes. Can you guess who they are?

676 "Ted"?
677 "Jocky"?
678 "Snoddy"?
679 "Gazzer"?
680 "Mitch"?
681 "Jeebs"?
682 "Kano"?

Fill in the blanks to discover the Hibees' names

683 – – R – – H   – – A – –
684 – – C – E –   – E – –
685 – R – H – –   – I – C – – L –
686 – – – N   – N – D – O –
687 – N – –   – O – A –
688 – – – D – –   – A –

Hibs visited these grounds in 1987/88 season. Who were they playing?

689 Brockville.
690 Tannadice.
691 East End Park.
692 Boghead.
693 Cappielow.
694 Fir Park.
695 Pittodrie.
696 Dens Park.
697 Love Street.
698 Parkhead.
699 George McCluskey used to play for Leeds United. Can you name the other 1987/88 Hibee who was also with the Elland Road club?

Can you help these mixed-up 1987/88 Hibees to find their real names?

700 RON LEIR.
701 NEIL CAMMUL.
702 NODY WASTAN.
703 NOT JOE TOROLA.
704 MAD YEDIE.

705 Hearts in their mouths! Name the goalscorer in this 7-0 thrashing of a certain Gorgie Road club in January 1973.

706 Not a murmur in the Hearts end as No. 5 scores for Hibs in a 1979 Scottish Cup tie. Can you name the scorer?

707 What was the result of that match?

DERBY DAZE

708 What is generally accepted as being the very first occasion on which Hibernian played Hearts?

709 When did Hibs achieve their first victory over Heart of Midlothian?

710 What was the winning scoreline in the above game and where was the match played?

711 The great Edinburgh rivals have clashed in a Scottish Cup final only once. When, and what was the match result?

712 Historically speaking, in what way is that famous final unique?

713 What agreement did Hibs and Hearts reach before they played that historic match?

714 Bobby Baxter played for both Hibs and Hearts . . . with which other club was he playing when capped in three full international matches?

715 Can you name two of the three Hibernian internationalists who later managed Hearts?

716 Can you name the three players who each scored a hat-trick against Hearts this century in Scottish League matches, (excluding wartime fixtures)?

717 Who scored four goals against the Maroons at Tynecastle in a 1958 Scottish Cup tie and what was the match result?

718 What was the score ten minutes after the kick-off when Hearts and Hibs met at Tynecastle in September 1965?

719 Can you recall the names of the players who scored for Hibernian on that auspicious occasion?

720 Which former Celtic player scored for both clubs in the match played at Tynecastle during April 1987?

721 Excluding own goals, can you name three of the four players who have scored for both sides in League "derbies"?

722 Hibs thrashed Hearts 7-0 at Tynecastle in 1973. Can you recall the names of the goalscoring heroes on that unforgettable occasion?

723 What was the score when the Edinburgh "giants" met at Easter Road in September 1966 and what was the significance of the match result?

724 Who scored Hibernian's winner in the 1-0 Ne'erday 1968 victory and why was the result significant?

725 Who scored a dramatic equaliser for Hibs in the dying seconds of a match played at Tynecastle in November 1975?

726 Who scored Hibs' winner in the 1-0 victory at Easter Road in August 1975?

727 The "Jam Tarts" were forced to eat humble pie again when Hibs won 1-0 at Tynecastle in January 1977. Who scored the Hibees' matchwinner?

728 What was the result of the 1976 Ne'erday match, and can you name the scorers?

729 Which trophy was "up for grabs" when Hibs and Hearts met at Easter Road on 9 August 1982?

730 Hibs were 1-0 victors in that August 1982 game. Who scored the winning goal for the home side?

731 Who was Hibs' matchwinner when the clubs clashed at Tynecastle in a February 1971 Scottish Cup tie?

732 **Including Hearts players, which individual has scored most league goals for his club in the big Edinburgh "derby"?**

733 Hibs beat Hearts 4-2 at Tynecastle in an October 1957 friendly. Who was Hibs' hat-trick hero on that occasion?

734 In which pre-season competition did Hibs beat Hearts 2-1 on 4 August 1979?

735 The Edinburgh rivals shared four goals in the last Rosebery Charity Cup final which was played at Easter Road in May 1945 . . . how was the match outcome decided?

736 This fellow scored only one first-team League goal during season 1976/77 and it came in a 1-1 draw v Hearts at Easter Road in October 1976. Can you name him?

737 In August 1944 a Hibs-Hearts select met a top English club in the first of a series of annual charity matches. Who were those visitors and what was the name of the trophy?

738 In October 1987 Paul Kane scored the winner in a 2-1 win over Hearts. Who scored the other Hibernian goal?

739 Can you recall how Hibs fared in the 1983 New Year fixture?

740 Which player came on as a sub in the March 1985 Tynecastle match when Hibs were trailing 0-2 and scored twice to salvage a point?

741 The same player was on target again in both the August 1986 and November 1986 fixtures. What were the match results?

742 Hibs and Hearts drew 2-2 at Easter Road in January 1987. Can you name the Hibernian goalscorers?

743 Can you name the first six players in this line-up
photographed in Augsberg during a May 1950 tour of
Germany, Austria and Switzerland?

744 Hibs won five of their six matches. Which team beat them?

745 What was the score when Hibs played Bayern Munich on 14
May?

746 The Duke of Edinburgh meets Hibs . . . what was the year and the occasion?

747 Can you name the players (including the fellow who's keeking over the Duke's shoulder)?

748 What was the result of the match?

749 Who scored for Hibs?

FRIENDLIES, TESTIMONIALS AND TOURS

750 Hibs and Bolton Wanderers drew 2-2 on 26 April 1952. Can you name the famous international centre-forwards who scored two goals apiece?

751 What was the scoreline when Bolton revisited Easter Road in October 1959?

752 Hibernian toured this country in the summer of 1962 and were undefeated in five matches.

753 Can you name the famous Austrian visitors who beat Hibs twice at Easter Road in the 1950s?

754 Hibernian beat Bayern Munich 3-2 in Germany during a 1960 tour. Can you name the centre-forward with the initials "JB" who scored two of the Hibs goals?

755 Bayern visited Easter Road in 1958 and 1960 . . . what was the same scoreline by which the Germans were beaten on each occasion?

756 What was the match result when Hibs played host to the famous Moscow Dynamo in February 1985 and who was the Hibees matchwinner?

757 Which Spanish team beat Hibs 3-1 at Easter Road on 21 November 1962?

758 Can you name the Dutch side beaten 3-0 in Edinburgh on 5 May 1971?

759 What was the score when Hibs played Liverpool at Easter Road in September 1956, and which famous Scottish winger scored for the opposition?

760 Liverpool and Hibs drew 3-3 at Anfield in November 1957. Can you name the Hibernian goalscorers on that occasion?

761 Why was Joe Harper a happy little chap when Dutch side Nijmegen visited Edinburgh on 5 August 1974?

762 Who did Hibs beat 15-1 during a 1965 tour of Canada and America?

763 What was the scoreline when Ottawa All Stars played host to Hibs on the same tour of North America?

764 Hibernian won all nine matches played during that 1965 summer tour. Which English club supplied the most formidable opposition and what was the match result?

765 Who scored the Hibernian goal in the 1-1 draw versus Manchester United which was played at Easter Road on Boxing Day 1981?

766 English Champions, Derby County, were the visitors for Hibs' centenary match played on 4 August 1975. Which Scottish internationalist scored the only goal of the game?

767 Eddie Turnbull was Hibs' manager at the time of that centenary match. Why had Eddie been a happier fellow when the same clubs met at Derby in October 1953?

768 Which American club did Hibs beat at Easter Road in October 1981 and what was the score?

769 Which famous star lined up for the "Yanks" in that match and which ex-Scotland player was the visitors' coach?

770 Can you name the Dutch opposition beaten 4-2 at Easter Road in December 1985?

771 What was the scoreline when Hibs played host to Leeds United in March 1957?

772 Which famous player scored a hat-trick for the Yorkshire club in that match?

773 What was the match result when Hibs and Manchester United clashed at Easter Road in September 1955?

774 Can you name the Polish visitors who beat Hibs 2-1 on 8 December 1969?

775 What was the significance of that defeat?

776 Can you recall the scoreline when Hibs travelled to York for an August 1971 friendly?

777 What was the match result when Hibernian and Tottenham Hotspur met at White Hart Lane on 25 April 1949?

778 What was the scoreline when the Hibs lads returned to London to play Spurs on 1 May 1950?

779 Can you name the international player who scored the Hibs goal in that 1950 match?

780 What was the outcome of a Spurs v Hibs game played in London on 23 April 1952?

781 . . . But it was a different ball game when the Londoners came north to play Hibs in September 1956. What was the result on this occasion?

782 You'd think they would be sick of the sight of each other, but Spurs were back in Edinburgh in October 1957. Which team won and who was the goalscoring hero?

783 Why did Doncaster Rovers invite Hibs to play them in March 1952 and what was the match result?

784 What was the match result when Hibs played Manchester City at Maine Road on 8 March 1952?

785 Who was the goalscoring hero in that Maine Road friendly?

786 What was the score when Hibs returned to Manchester later

in the same month . . . this time to face United at Old Trafford?

787 Can you identify the two players missing from the Hibs defence which played in the 2-0 victory v Real Madrid in 1964? Wilson, Fraser and – – – – – – –; Stanton, – – – – – – – – – and Baxter.

788 Can you name the Yugoslavian goalkeeper who played for Hibs in a 3-2 win against Leicester City in December 1979?

789 Can you name the player who scored a hat-trick in Hibernian's 4-1 win over Chelsea at Easter Road in August 1986?

790 What was the scoreline when Notts Forest visited Easter Road in August 1966 and which ex-Hib scored for the visitors?

791 Joe Harper and John Brownlie scored Hibernian's goals v these Hibs in July 1975. Who were they?

792 Which Spanish team did Hibs play home and away in 1986, what were the scores and who was the opposition manager?

793 Who scored a hat-trick v Middlesbrough at Easter Road in November 1959 and what was the match result?

794 Can you name the English international centre-forward who played for Middlesbrough in that game?

795 What was the outcome of a return match played at Middlesbrough ten days later?

796 Against which club did Ally Brazil score a January 1985 hat-trick and what was the match result?

797 Hibs and "Pompey" drew 3-3 at Fratton Park in May 1960. Can you name the opponents?

798 What was the scoreline when Hibs met Celtic on 30 April 1978 in the Pat Stanton testimonial match?

799 Who scored the winning goal from the penalty spot in that benefit game?

800 Against which English club did Ally MacLeod score twice in a 3-0 win at Easter Road in September 1977?

801 Ally scored the only goal of a match played at Selhurst Park in February 1978. Can you name the opponents?

802 Who were the Brazilians beaten 3-1 at Easter Road in April 1956?

803 Which city did Hibs adopt as their "home" for a series of matches played in Canada and America in the summer of 1967?

804 Can you name the Brazilians who drew 1-1 with Hibs in America in 1967?

805 The venue for that match v the Brazilians is famous for staging world heavyweight boxing title fights. Where was the game played?

806 Which team beat Hibs 1-0 at Easter Road in the September 1948 Willie McCartney memorial match?

807 What was the match result when Hibs played host to Sunderland in August 1981?

808 Sunderland revisited Easter Road in February 1983. What was the scoreline and which future Hibs player scored for the Roker Park side?

809 An ex-Hibee, who later rejoined the club, was also included in that Sunderland line-up. Can you name him?

810 Hibs played under primitive floodlights before the turn of the century . . . but where and against whom did they play their first match under real lights?

811 When was the first floodlit match staged at Easter Road, and who were Hibs' opponents on that historic occasion?

812 Within days of that first floodlit match in Edinburgh, Hibs and "The Royals" drew 2-2 under the Elm Park lights. Who are they?

813 Can you give the scoreline when Hibs played a Scotland XI at Easter Road in the December 1958 Lawrie Reilly testimonial match?

814 An International XI provided the opposition for Arthur Duncan's testimonial game in May 1981. What was the result and which Charlie scored twice for the opposition?

815 Can you name this late 1930's forward line?

816 The Hibs eleven who played Aberdeen in the 1947 Scottish Cup final . . . how many do you recognise?

817 Can you spot an ex-Hibs player tending his garden in the 1960s?

818 To which club did Hibernian pay £25,000 for the transfer of the wee lad with the wheelbarrow in January 1985?

819 There's a member of Hibs' "Famous Five" forward line somewhere in this 1936/37 Falkirk and District Schools team. Can you spot him?

820 Also in the team line-up are two members of Rangers' "Iron Curtain" defence who were among the "Five's" greatest rivals. Can you also spot them?

The "Famous Five" were, undoubtedly, the greatest club forward line in the history of British football . . . Gordon Smith, Bobby Johnstone, Lawrie Reilly, Eddie Turnbull and Willie Ormond were the perfect blend. More than anything else they enjoyed playing the game . . . and it showed! They moved in instinctive and ever-changing football patterns which were way beyond the comprehension of the authors of the coaching manual. Sharing a great personal friendship and mutual admiration which has endured to this day, though deeply saddened by the passing of Willie Ormond, these heroes collected 83 caps between them while at Easter Road . . . and in an era when such honours were fewer and very much harder to come by! "Attack" was the most important word in their soccer vocabulary, as they proved by scoring over 1500 goals between them. The "Five" were the glittering jewel in mighty Hibernian's crown. Were they still playing today they would be absolutely priceless!

821 The "Famous Five" first played as a forward line in a competitive match on 15 October 1949 and Hibs won 2-0. Can you name the opposition? Was it – *A*: East Fife *B*: Raith Rovers *C*: Queen of the South.

PICTURE QUIZ

Personal favourites. The following 13 players wore the club colours with style and distinction. They, and many others, have made me feel proud to be a supporter of Hibernian Football Club.

822 In which year did the great Gordon Smith become a Hibernian player?

823 On 28 April 1941 Smith scored a hat-trick on his debut for the club. Who were the opponents and what was the score?

824 Why will Gordon never forget Hibs' home game v Third Lanark on 8 November 1947?

825 Smith is the club's leading scorer in all games. Did he score – A: 285 goals   B: 364 goals   C: 319 goals?

826 How many times did Gordon Smith play for Scotland and against which country did he make his international debut?

827 Who were Hibs' opponents in the Gordon Smith testimonial match played in September 1952 and what was the match result?

828 In which year was Gordon Smith voted Scottish football's "Player of the Year"?

829 An unhappy day . . . but where and when did this marvellous club servant play his last game in the green and white of Hibernian?

One of British football's all-time greats, this wonder winger set standards which have never been surpassed and rarely equalled . . . those who saw him play should regard themselves as privileged!

830 From which Junior club did Bobby join Hibs in 1946?

831 How many times did he represent Scotland at full international level?

832 Against which country did he make a scoring international debut?

833 How much did Manchester City pay for his transfer in March 1955? A: £18,000 B: £22,000 C: £24,000.

834 Which rare distinction did Johnstone achieve as a City player?

835 When did Bobby return to Easter Road and how much did the club pay for his transfer?

836 Just over a year later and this great favourite was off on his travels again . . . which Lancashire club did he join for a £3,000 fee?

A highly skilled ball player, this little genius of an inside-forward enjoys favourable comparison with any of the illustrious stars who have graced the position. Bobby loved to display his vast range of talents on the big stage. He once told me: "If you can't play football at Wembley you can't play football".

97

837 In which year did Lawrie Reilly become a Hibernian player?

838 Reilly is Hibs' top marksman in League matches. Did he score – A: 196 goals   B: 163 goals   C: 187 goals?

839 Lawrie is also Hibernian's most-capped player. How many times did he play for Scotland at full international level?

840 How many goals did this great player score in his five appearances at Wembley?

841 In which year did Lawrie score both Scottish goals in a 2-2 draw at Wembley and why was the second goal memorable?

842 Reilly earned undying fame as a centre-forward, but in which other position did he win seven of his full caps?

843 Against which club did Lawrie score seven goals in two League matches during season 1952/53?

844 In what way was Lawrie Reilly unique among the "Famous Five" forward line?

845 The famous cry "Gie the ba' tae Reilly" was heard for the last time in April 1958. Who were Hibs' opponents when Lawrie took his final bow?

846 Can you recall the match result and the Hibernian scorers on that emotional occasion?

A marvellous Hibs servant, the darting and deadly goalscorer is one of the truly great legends of Scottish football. Lawrie Reilly proved his pedigree at the very highest level . . . he transformed Wembley into a back-door graveyard for the "Auld Enemy".

847 When did Eddie Turnbull become a Hibernian player?

848 How many times did he play for Scotland at full international level?

849 Against which country did Eddie make his international debut?

850 Against which club did Eddie Turnbull score four League goals on 4 February 1950?

851 How many times did Turnbull score a hat-trick for Hibs in competitive matches? *A*: 10 times *B*: 17 times *C*: 8 times.

852 In which position did this great club servant play when he captained Hibs in the 1958 Scottish Cup final?

853 Which role did Eddie fulfil at Easter Road after "hanging up his boots" in 1959?

854 Which club did Turnbull join as a coach in June 1963?

855 When did Eddie Turnbull vacate the manager's chair at Aberdeen to take over control at Easter Road?

856 When did Eddie resign the position of Hibernian manager?

A real grafter, a great player and a fine manager, Eddie has done as much for Hibs' cause as anyone in the history of the club. The man has earned the undying gratitude of Hibernian Football Club.

857 From which club did Hibernian sign Willie Ormond in November 1946?

858 At the start of season 1958/59 Hibs had 39 players on the payroll. In what way was Ormond unique?

859 How many times did this great little winger play for Scotland at full international level?

860 Where and when did Willie play his last game for Hibs?

861 Why was 7 October 1961 a day of mixed emotions for Willie?

862 Can you name the clubs which Willie Ormond managed?

863 When did he become Scotland's international team manager?

864 Which honour did Willie Ormond receive in 1975?

865 In what capacity did Willie come "home" to Easter Road in March 1980?

Despite a succession of serious injuries, this brave little winger always bounced back to the very top of the ladder. A tricky, highly talented player and a fine manager, Willie's name should be printed in capital letters in the Scottish football "Hall of Fame".

866 In which English city was Joe Baker born?

867 Although an England player, Joe was also a Scottish Schoolboy internationalist: True/False?

868 Which club did Joe join as a ground staff boy in the mid-Fifties while still at school?

869 How many times did Joe Baker play for England at senior level, and against which country did he make a scoring international debut?

870 How many goals did Joe score for Hibs in competitive matches. A: 159   B: 126   C: 143

871 Why did Joe and the supporters enjoy a very merry Christmas in 1960?

872 How many goals did Baker score against Peebles Rovers in Hibernian's 1961 record Scottish Cup win?

873 How much did Italian club Torino pay for the transfer of Joe Baker in 1961

874 Which famous Scottish internationalist was a Torino team-mate of Baker's?

875 Can you name the six senior clubs for which this great centre-forward played?

876 When did Joe come "home" to a hero's welcome, and against which club did he make a scoring debut on his return?

Joe was a centre-forward who struck like lightning and, as often as not, more than once in the same place. Having spent the first six weeks of his life in England, Baker played his international matches in the famous white shirt . . . he had no choice in those days! A natural and exciting goalscorer, Joe is one of the best-loved players in the history of the club.

877 How much did Hibs pay Hearts for the transfer of Willie Hamilton in October 1963? *A*: £8,000   *B*: £6,000   *C*: £7,500

878 Against which country did Hamilton win his only full cap?

879 Willie once scored seven goals for Hibs. When and against whom?

880 Against which club did he score two Scottish Cup goals in March 1965?

881 Can you name the five senior clubs for which Willie played?

882 To which of these clubs was he transferred for £25,000 in August 1965?

A wayward genius, Willie Hamilton was endowed with a football talent which is far removed from the pages of the coaching manual. The sight of this delectable inside-forward mesmerising both Ferenc Puskas of Real Madrid and Jim Baxter of Rangers within the space of three October days in 1964 is something which will be forever etched on my memory. True footballing genius is a gift bestowed on precious few players ... the late, great Willie Hamilton was one such player.

883 Which manager signed Pat for Hibs in 1963?

884 Against which club did Stanton make a scoring first-team debut on 5 October 1963?

885 Against which club did he score his only hat-trick in a competitive match?

886 How many times did he play for Scotland at full international level?

887 Against which country did he make his international debut?

888 In which year was Pat Stanton voted "Player of the Year" by the Scottish Football Writers' Association?

889 Which player was involved in the swop deal which sent Stanton to Celtic Park in September 1976?

890 Apart from Hibs, can you name two other clubs which Pat Stanton has managed?

891 When did he become Hibernian's manager?

892 When did he vacate the post?

893 Which highly knowledgeable Scotland team manager described Pat as being "A better player than Bobby Moore"?

A great personal favourite, Pat's talents shone out like a beacon across Easter Road for 13 years . . . Yes . . . the "King of Easter Road" supplied me with countless unforgettable memories, but perhaps I will best recall that day in December 1972 when this fine athlete surged through the Celtic midfield time after time building wave after wave of Hibernian attacks which eventually submerged the Celts and saw Pat climb those famous Hampden steps to lift the Scottish League Cup. Versatile and highly talented, in my book Pat Stanton was our greatest-ever captain.

894 When and where did Peter Cormack make a scoring first-team debut for Hibs?

895 How many times did Peter play for Scotland at full international level?

896 Against which famous footballing nation did Cormack make his Scotland debut?

897 Against which club did he score a hat-trick in a December 1968 League match?

898 To which club was Peter transferred for £80,000 in March 1970?

899 For which other senior clubs did this highly talented and successful footballer play?

900 When and where did Peter make his debut for the club the second time around?

901 When did Peter arrive at Easter Road for the third time to take up the appointment of Assistant Manager to Alex Miller?

902 Do the youngsters know for which club Peter was playing when the photograph was taken?

Another great Hibee, Peter Cormack was a highly gifted player who, like Bobby Johnstone, demonstrated his considerable skills on both sides of the Border to such effect that he won universal acclaim. Peter was one of the finest footballers who ever donned the famous green and white jersey of Hibernian.

111

903 From which club did Hibs sign John Blackley in 1965?

904 How many times did he represent Scotland at full international level?

905 Against which country did John make his international debut?

906 How much did Newcastle pay for his transfer in October 1977? Was it – A: £75,000   B: £120,000   C: £100,000

907 Can you name the other senior clubs for which he played?

908 When did Blackley become Hibernian's manager?

909 When did he resign the post?

910 John was a superstitious player . . . what did he do before kick-off in every match?

A highly polished performer, John made the difficult things look easy because he was a great positional player and "reader" of the game. Another Hibee who proved his ability at the very highest level, John timed his tackles to absolute perfection and enjoyed the utmost respect of friend and foe alike.

911 From which junior club did Hibs sign John Brownlie in 1969?

912 How many times did this marvellous full-back appear for Scotland in full international matches?

913 Against which country did he win his first full cap and, from a club viewpoint, what was the significance of that honour?

914 Which player came to Easter Road in an August 1978 swop deal which sent Brownlie to Newcastle United?

915 For which other English-based senior clubs did he play?

Having established himself as the finest young full-back in Britain, John tragically broke a leg in January 1973. But this whole-hearted player bounced back to the top in determined fashion and nobody who ever saw him play will forget his surging, cavalier-style runs down the right wing. Highly skilled and defensively sound, Brownlie was one of the classiest and most constructive full-backs in the history of Scottish football.

916 To which club did Hibs pay £35,000 for the transfer of Arthur Duncan in January 1970?

917 Against which club did Arthur score four League goals on 23 October 1971?

918 Why would Arthur be particularly interested in the half-time scoreboard on that same October Saturday?

919 Against which club did he score three League goals in November 1975 and what was the significance of that hat-trick?

920 How many times did Arthur play for Scotland at full international level?

921 Against which country did this great Hibee make his international debut?

922 After 14 years' marvellous service both as a winger and a full-back, which club did Arthur join in 1984?

Arthur always seemed to have a smile on his face, and that happy attitude was reflected in his play. The Easter Road "flyer" was one of Hibs' greatest-ever servants . . . a marvellous wing-forward, this popular fellow proved his versatility when he stepped back to fill the left-back berth towards the end of a distinguished career.

Possessing great skill and balance as a playmaker coupled with a natural goalscoring flair, Ally is included in my thirteen personal favourite Hibees because he was a player who, to use his own expression, "could make the ball do the work". There is no substitute for sheer football skill, and Ally had it in abundance . . . he was a joy to watch.

118

923 Against which opposition did Ally represent the Scottish League in 1980?

924 Ally MacLeod was a prolific scorer when goals were in short supply. How many times did he score for Hibs in competitive matches? *A*: 99 times *B*: 88 times *C*: 76 times

925 Ally was the club's highest scorer in competitive matches over five consecutive seasons: True/False?

926 Against which English club did this marvellous footballer score a hat-trick in a 3-2 home win for Hibs on 10 December 1979?

927 With which club did Ally have a brief association before retiring in 1982?

NICKNAMES (3)

Hibs' marvellous League Cup-winning side of 1972 all had nicknames. How many do you know?

928 Jim Herriot?
929 John Brownlie?
930 Erich Schaedler?
931 Pat Stanton?
932 Jim Black?
933 John Blackley?
934 Alex Edwards?
935 Jim O'Rourke?
936 Alan Gordon?
937 Alex Cropley?
938 Arthur Duncan?
939 . . . and manager, Eddie Turnbull?

940 Hibs' photo-call at the start of season 1987/88 . . . can you recognise all the faces?

941 At the time the picture was taken, which six players had never been attached to any other senior club?

942 Which two players in the line-up were signed from Aberdeen?

943 Which player was transferred to Dunfermline Athletic not long after this picture was taken?

944 Can you spot the forward who once played for Leeds United?

945 Fill in the missing names in this 1958 line-up. *Back row left
     to right* McLeod, ..., McLelland, ...,
     Paterson, Turnbull, Plenderleith, ... *Front row
     left to right* . . . ., ..., Baker, Reilly,
     . . . . and Ormond.
946 Can you name the three players in this group who did not
     play in the 1958 Cup final v Clyde?

947 At the start of which season was this the Hibernian player pool?

948 How many of the faces do you recognise?

949 Can you name three English-born players in this line-up?

950 Can you name this line-up pictured in July 1981?

951 What is the trophy?

952 After leaving Easter Road three of the players in the group joined Hamilton Academical. Who are they?

953 . . . And two of the men in the photograph became manager of the "Accies". Who are they?

954 Past masters photographed at Easter Road in August 1971
. . . who are they and what was the occasion?

955 Mechelen won the European Cup Winners Cup in 1988. Can you name two ex-Hibees who played for the Belgian club in the 1960s?

956 Can you name the four former Hibs players who are the owners of a coveted European Cup Winner's medal?

957 Can you name the Scots comedian/singer who recorded *Glory, Glory to the Hibees* in the 1960s?

958 What is widely accepted in the best circles as being the "B" side of that recording?

959 This famous forward scored four goals v Queen of the South in an August 1946 League match and four more v Alloa in a January 1947 Scottish Cup tie.

960 This marvellous 1960's forward was even quicker on the draw, scoring four goals in consecutive matches v Alloa and Falkirk in September 1965.

961 Andy Goram joined Oldham Athletic in 1981, but with which Midlands club was he once an apprentice player?

962 Who scored both Hibernian goals in a 2-0 win over Celtic at Easter Road on 19 September 1970?

963 What was the significance of that 1970 victory over the Celts?

964 Who were the *Scotsman* describing in this 1966 obituary? – "Spectators should raise their eyes to the floodlights and remember that it was . . . . who pioneered them. They should think on the excitement of European Cup football and remember that it was . . . . who led Scotland into Europe against fierce opposition."

965 Which famous boxer was guest of honour at the Hibs v Falkirk match in September 1971?

966 Which ex-Celt scored the only goal of the game against his former club at Parkhead on 16 September 1978?

967 In which season did Hibs beat Rangers twice in the League as well as in a Scottish Cup tie?

968 What was the significance of that double League win?

969 This central defender was signed from Dundee in 1976 and joined Cowdenbeath in October 1980.

970 Which team did Hibs beat 9-1 on 10 August 1946 in the first competitive fixture played after the war?

971 Can you name the goalkeeper who played for all three Edinburgh clubs which are currently members of the Scottish League?

972 Can you name the ex-Hearts player who made a scoring debut for Hibs against St Mirren at Love Street in a July 1979 Anglo-Scottish Cup tie?

973 Where and against whom did a Norwegian score for Hibs in a December 1978 friendly?

974 Can you name the other Norwegian player who was with Hibs for a short spell in season 1978/79?

975 Hibs were beaten 3-2 by both Rangers and Celtic in the autumn of 1982. Who scored all four Hibernian goals?

976 Which famous player made his Hibernian debut in that November 1982 defeat by Celtic?

977 Des Bremner scored one of Hibs' goals in a 2-0 win at Ibrox in August 1977. Can you name the youngster who scored the other goal on his first appearance v Rangers?

978 Gordon Marshall and Ralph Callachan played for Hibs and Hearts . . . for which other club did they both play?

979 Marshall and Chris Shevlane played for the big Edinburgh clubs . . . for which other Scottish League team did both play?

980 Hibs and Rangers drew 1-1 at Easter Road in March 1978. Who scored Hibs' goal from the penalty spot and which former Hibs man was in the Rangers line-up?

981 Who scored a double for Celtic v Hibs at Parkhead on 5 April 1978?

982 Can you name the youngster who played for the first team in three Highland tour matches v Brora, Keith and Inverness Thistle in the summer of 1980 when aged only 15?

983 Can you name the winger with the initials "WM" who scored on his debut v Waterford (Eire) in July 1972?

984 Can you name the two Hibees who played in both the 3-2 win v Barcelona in February 1961 and the 2-0 win v Real Madrid in October 1964?

985 Where and when did John Collins make his competitive first-team debut for the club?

986 Can you name the player who scored six hat-tricks for Hibs between January 1940 and March 1941?

987 Who scored the only goal of the game v St Mirren at Easter Road in January 1987?

988 Which former Hibs player captained Bristol City to their Freight Rovers Trophy win at Wembley in May 1986?

989 Can you name the Hibs goalscorers v Rangers on 9 August 1986 when a certain player took an early bath on his Premier League debut day?

990 Can you name the current Scottish League club who were founded in 1909 as . . . . Hibernians?

991 Hibs and Airdrie drew 1-1 at Easter Road in an August 1982 League Cup tie. Can you name the centre-half who scored his only first-team goal for the club in the final minute of that match?

992 Can you name the player who headed the first goal in a 2-0 Premier League victory over Dunfermline at Easter Road in February 1988?

993 Which ex-Celt played for Hibs, as a substitute, v Celtic in the 1972 Scottish Cup final?

994 Why was 16 January 1971 an unlucky day for Aberdeen and Scotland goalkeeper Bobby Clark?

995 Why was Saturday, 28 September 1974 a day of mixed emotions for Jimmy O'Rourke?

996 Against which club did Hibs score 14 goals in two League matches during season 1952/53?

997 Can you name the full-back who scored Hibs' first goal v Napoli in November 1967?

998 Which club did ex-Hib Ronnie Simpson manage in the early 1970s?

999 Which club did former Hibs centre-half Roy Barry manage in the late 1970s?

1000 Can you name the ex-Celt who scored his only European goal in the club's 3-2 UEFA Cup win over Norrköping in September 1978?

1001 Which player scored Hibs' other goals in that 1978 match versus the Swedes?

1002 Can you name the young player with the initials "HH" who scored Hibs' goal v Alloa in a 1-1 Bell's League Cup match played at Easter Road in August 1980?

1003 Can you name the former "Auld Reekie" rivals who shocked Hibs by winning 3-2 at Easter Road in a 1937/38 Scottish Cup tie?

1004 When did Jimmy O'Rourke return to Easter Road in a coaching capacity?

1005 Hibs signed Rikki Fleming from Ayr United in 1978, but for which Glasgow club did he once play?

1006 Hibernian beat "The Lilywhites" 4-0 in an October 1955 friendly. Who are they?

1007 Whom did David Duff succeed as club Chairman in August 1987?

1008 Can you name the clubs Walter Galbraith managed prior to joining Hibernian?

1009 Can you name the last club for which Erich Schaedler played?

1010 From which club did Tommy Craig join Hibernian as a player/coach in October 1984?

1011 Fill in missing names . . . forward line v Real Madrid in 1964: Cormack, Hamilton, ... , Quinn and . . . .

1012 Hibs beat Hamilton 11-1 in 1965. Can you name the ex-Easter Road player in the "Accies" line-up?

1013 Barcelona left-back Jesus Garay was no angel. Which player did he foul when Hibs were awarded that famous penalty in 1961?

1014 Who scored both goals in a 1962 2-0 victory over Bolton at Easter Road?

1015 Who took over the club chairmanship from Harry Swan in August 1963?

1016 Against which club did that marvellous full-back, Bobby Duncan, break a leg in January 1968?

1017 Another great right-back, against which club did John Brownlie break his leg in January 1973?

1018 To which club was Bobby Thomson transferred in September 1985?

1019 A 1970's picture of a Hibee in action . . . who? An easy one, but photograph is included as a tribute to a marvellous footballer.

1020 Smile please . . . it's 1971 and Joe Baker is "home". Can you name the happy Hibees?

FINAL WHISTLE

1021 Who, at a May 1988 press conference, described Hibernian as "A sleeping giant which is about to wake up"?

Answers

JUST FOR STARTERS

1   David Duff on taking over the chairmanship of the club.

KICK-OFF

2   1875.
3   11-1 v Hamilton Academical 6 November 1965.
4   11-1 v Airdrieonians 24 October 1959.
5   Peebles Rovers.
6   22-1 v 42nd Highlanders (h) 3 September 1881.
7   1887 and 1902.
8   Eight times.
9   Four times.
10 In season 1950/51 (Rangers were second).
11 Season 1959/60 . . . 106.
12 Season 1980/81 when 57 points were amassed in the First Division.
13 Gordon Smith.
14 Season 1972/73.
15 Arthur Duncan (446).
16 Joe Harper v Hearts (30 August 1975).
17 Two points.
18 Versus Clyde at Shawfield (11 April 1951).
19 Dundee (9 April 1952).

FRESH IN THE MEMORY?

20 Rotherham United, and he once played for Coventry City.
21 Dundee (Hibs won 2-1).
22 Luton Town, £200,000.
23 Against St Mirren at Easter Road.
24 Versus Celtic at Parkhead.
25 St Mirren.
26 Orlando Lions, USA.
27 Montrose . . . Hibs won 3-2.

28 Queen of the South, and debutant Neil Orr scored one of the goals.
29 Motherwell and Andy Watson.
30 Paul Kane . . . Dunfermline 3 Hibernian 3.
31 Gordon Marshall of Falkirk.
32 Dundee United.
33 Versus St Mirren at Love Street in October 1987 (2-2).
34 **Paul Kane (1-1).**
35 Andy Watson.
36 Hibs beat Rangers 1-0 at Easter Road.
37 John Collins.
38 Paul Kane and Joe Tortolano.
39 Shrewsbury Town.
40 Falkirk at Brockville in October 1987 (1-1).
41 Goalkeeper Andy Goram scored direct from a clearance.
42 Sheila Rowland.
43 £300,000
44 He was voted Young Player of the Year by the Scottish Professional Footballers' Association.
45 Dundee (H) 2-1, Motherwell (A) 2-0, Dunfermline (H) 2-0.
46 Danny Lennon.
47 Blackburn Rovers (on loan), Barcelona, Tottenham Hotspur, Aberdeen and Clyde.
48 Tottenham Hotspur.

PICTURE QUIZ

49 £325,000
50 Dunfermline . . . Hibs won 4-0.
51 A: 16.

FIRST NAMES

52 Bobby.
53 Derek.
54 Jimmy.
55 Johnny.
56 Rab.
57 George.

58 Tommy.
59 Harvey.
60 Bobby.
61 Harry.
62 Jimmy.
63 George.
64 Malcolm.
65 Alex.
66 John.
67 Joe.
68 Jimmy.
69 Eric.
70 John.
71 Willie.
72 Jimmy.
73 Gary.
74 Gerry.
75 Robin.
76 Hugh.
77 Roy.
78 Derek.
79 William.
80 Duncan.
81 Bobby.
82 Robert (he preferred Robert to Bobby).
83 Arthur.
84 Calum.
85 Duncan.
86 Davie.
87 Angus.
88 Alex.
89 Colin.
90 Willie.
91 Alex.
92 Bobby.
93 Willie.
94 Joe.
95 Gerry.

96 Johnny.
97 Andy.
98 Michael.
99 Billy.
100 Mike.
101 Kevin.

PICTURE QUIZ

102 *Left to right* : Paul Kane, Gordon Hunter and Gordon Durie.

PICTURE QUIZ

103 *Left to right* : Trainer Jimmy McColl, Pat Ward, Tommy D'Arcy, Tommy Younger and Willie McFarlane.
104 Willie McFarlane.

DATELINE

105 Alan Gordon scores extra-time winner v Celtic in Drybrough Cup final (1- 0).
106 Eddie May nets winner in a marvellous Scottish Cup victory over Celtic at Easter Road . . . Hibs 4 Celtic 3.
107 Pat Stanton scores one and makes one as Hibs beat the Celts in the League Cup final.
108 Hibernian beat Dumbarton 2-1 at second. Hampden Park to win the Scottish Cup for the first time.
109 Hibs are surprisingly beaten 3-0 by Motherwell in the League Cup final.
110 The Hibees absolutely annihilate Hearts 7-0 at Tynecastle. (They'll never be allowed to live that one down.)
111 Rheims beat Hibs 2-0 in European Cup semi-final 1st leg.
112 Joe Harper whips one into the net for the only goal of the game v Falkirk in the League Cup semi-final at Tynecastle.
113 Hibernian beat Celtic 1-0 in the 29th Scottish Cup final.

114 Easter Road houses its biggest crowd (65,800 v Hearts).

115 Paul Kane scores winner in 2-1 victory over Hearts at Easter Road.

116 Lawrie Reilly gets both Scottish goals in a 2-2 draw at Wembley.

117 Dunfermline (The "Pars") beat Hibs 2-0 in Scottish Cup semi-final at Tynecastle.

118 Napoli are crushed 5-0 at Easter Road in the Fairs Cup.

119 George Best is happy to score on his debut despite a 2-1 defeat from St Mirren at Love Street.

120 Hibs hammer Ally McLeod's Ayr United 8-1 at Easter Road.

121 Joe Harper scores UEFA Cup 1st-leg winner versus Liverpool at Easter Road (1-0).

122 Back "home" after almost ten years, Joe Baker scores v Aberdeen in his first match (Hibs won 2-1).

123 Hibs beat Rangers 2-1 in Scottish Cup semi-final replay at Hampden.

124 Three days after beating Real Madrid, Hibs outplay Rangers and win 4-2 at Ibrox.

PICTURE QUIZ

125 Bobby Baxter.

PICTURE QUIZ

126 Joe Davin.
127 Morton.

CUP-TIE FEVER

128 P. Lafferty.

129 It was the first time the trophy had left the West of Scotland after 13 finals. Interestingly, that was the first final in which

both sides played in a 2-3-5 formation . . . a pattern which was to endure for many decades.

130 Hibernian 3 Dumbarton 0.

131 **Andy McGeechan.**

132 Celtic Park. The match was originally scheduled for the Rangers ground but was switched in the wake of the disaster which occurred at Ibrox when Scotland played England.

133 Hibernian 0 Celtic 1.

134 Allan McGraw.

135 Hibs beat Dundee 2-1.

136 Jim O'Rourke . . . Hibs won 2-0 at Easter Road.

137 Kilbowie Park, Clydebank . . . Hibs beat E.S. Clydebank 2-0.

138 Sadly, it was the only goal of the game against Celtic in the Hampden final.

139 Airdrie beat Hibs 2-0.

140 Ibrox. None . . . it was the last occasion on which a Scottish Cup final was played at a venue other than Hampden.

141 Dornan, Miller, McColl and Halligan.

142 Hugh Shaw.

143 John Baxter.

144 Jack Mowat.

145 Alex Miller.

146 Arthur Duncan . . . Sorry, Arthur – worse for you, but a sore moment for all of us!

147 Berwick Rangers . . . fresh from a famous victory over another Rangers in the previous round.

148 The teams drew 0-0 and Hibs took the trophy because they had won six corners to Rangers' five corners.

149 Kilbowie Park . . . Clydebank 1 Hibernian 0.

150 Rangers . . . it was the first time the Ibrox side had lost in the "Scottish" for four years (22 games).

151 Aberdeen . . . Johnny Cuthbertson.

152 Stan Williams.

153 Bobby Calder.

154 Hibs scored twice in extra time to beat Celtic 5-3 in the Drybrough Cup final, having been beaten 6-1 by the Parkhead team in the 1972 Scottish Cup final.

155 Jim O'Rourke and Arthur Duncan.

156 Hibs 1 Celtic 0 after extra time . . . Alan Gordon.

157 Ayr United . . . Hibs won 2-1 at home and drew 2-2 away.

158 Blackburn Rovers . . . Hibs won 2-1 at home and 1-0 away.

159 Bristol City . . . Hibs drew 1-1 at home and lost 3-5 away.

160 Tottenham Hotspur. Hibernian won 2-1 in replay after a 1-1 draw.

161 Newcastle United 0 Hibernian 4.

162 Celtic, who won 2-0.

163 Alan Gordon in a 3-3 draw. Dundee won replay 3-0.

164 Gordon Rae and Ally MacLeod (penalty).

165 Meadowbank Thistle. Hibs won 6-0.

166 Versus Rangers in the 1948 Scottish Cup semi-final at Hampden . . . Rangers won 1-0.

167 Hibernian 4 Aberdeen 2 . . . Willie Ormond broke a leg in 33 minutes. Immediately afterwards goalkeeper Jimmy Kerr damaged a hand and left the field with Sammy Kean taking over in goal. Nine-man Hibs battled on and Kerr returned as an outfield "passenger" . . . a remarkable victory!

168 Isak Refvik (Hibs won 2-1 on aggregate).

169 Cowdenbeath . . . Steve Cowan.

170 6-1 for Hibs . . . Gordon Durie.

171 Celtic . . . the teams drew 4-4 at Easter Road after extra time and Hibs won 4-3 on penalties.

172 Gordon Chisholm . . . Gordon Durie got the other and Hibs won 2-1 on aggregate.

173 Aberdeen 3 Hibernian 0.

174 Clyde.

175 The tie took a record two hours 22 minutes to complete . . . after extra time the sides were level at 1-1 and they embarked on a "sudden death" situation which ended when Hugh Howie scored the winner for the Easter Road men.

176 Hibs 3 Rangers 2.

177 The teams drew 0-0 after extra time and Rangers won the trophy on the toss of a coin.

178 Hibernian beat Aberdeen 3-1 at Pittodrie in a Summer Cup decider.

179 Joe Harper, when Celtic beat Hibs 6-3 in the 1974 League Cup final.
180 Bobby Johnstone.
181 John Fraser and Eddie Turnbull (penalty).
182 East Stirlingshire (h) . . . Paul Kane.
183 Hamilton Academical (a) . . . Stuart Beedie.
184 Ex-Hearts player Ralph Callachan scored v Meadowbank Thistle at Tynecastle.
185 Aberdeen.
186 Alex Cropley.
187 Montrose, (4-0).
188 On loan Doug Moran scored the winner v Kilmarnock . . . it could only happen to the Hibees!
189 Arthur Duncan.
190 Aberdeen won 4-1 at Pittodrie in a section match.
191 Queen's Park.
192 Dundee United (a), Jim O'Rourke (Hibs won 5-2 on aggregate).
193 Hibs won 6-2 (a) and 4-1 (h).
194 Arthur Duncan.
195 John Brownlie.
196 Pat Stanton and Jim O'Rourke . . . Kenny Dalglish.
197 Bobby Johnstone.

PICTURE QUIZ

198 Alan Gordon scores against Celtic in the 1972 Drybrough Cup final.
199 Hibernian 5 Celtic 3 (after extra time).

NICKNAMES

200 "Nicker".
201 "Benny".
202 "The Incredible Hulk".
203 "Bimbo".
204 "Primo" (after Primo Carnera).

205 "Dingy".
206 "The Gay Gordon".
207 "Ginger" (Dunn also known as "Tim").
208 "Cannon".
209 "The Uncrowned King of Gilmerton".

PICTURE QUIZ

210 Versus Dumbarton, League Cup 24 August 1983 and v St Johnstone League 19 November 1983.

PICTURE QUIZ

211 Willie McCartney.

FOOTBALL'S A FAMILY GAME

212 Big Gordon's dad . . . Tommy McQueen.
213 Jim and Alex Scott.
214 Gibson.
215 John Frye.
216 Pat Stanton.
217 Joe McBride.
218 Greenock Morton . . . Neil Orr also played for them.
219 Davie Shaw . . . brother Jock was capped four times while with Rangers.
220 Ronnie Simpson.
221 Lewis.
222 Joe and Gerry Baker.
223 John and Craig Paterson.
224 Duncan and John Lambie.
225 Erich Schaedler.
226 Murdo MacLeod.
227 Maley.
228 They are brothers-in-law.
229 Coach Martin Ferguson . . . brother Alex is, of course, manager of Manchester United.

230 Bob Shankly . . . brother Bill was, of course, the famous Liverpool manager.

231 Steve Cowan.
232 St Mirren and Aberdeen.
233 Motherwell.

234 Armadale Thistle and Arsenal.
235 Four times.
236 Versus England at Wembley in 1961.
237 The "Auld Enemy" won 9-3.
238 Partick Thistle.
239 Partick Thistle 2 Hibernian 10.

240 Jackie Plenderleith.

241 1941 . . . from Inveresk Athletic.
242 Rangers.
243 Hibernian 8 Rangers 1 (lovely!).
244 Three times.
245 Versus England at Hampden in April 1948, (0-2).
246 None . . . Bobby was a one-club man and a whole-hearted performer for 16 years.
247 Dumbarton.

248 The "blanket" was installed in 1981.

249 Pat Quinn v Clyde (a). 12 November 1966.

250 Dave Ewing.

251 Willie McCartney, Hugh Shaw, Willie McFarlane, Eddie Turnbull, Willie Ormond, Bertie Auld, Pat Stanton and John Blackley.

252 Tony Higgins.

253 Brian Marjoribanks.

254 George McNeill.

255 Jimmy Kerr and Tommy Younger.

256 Hanover.

257 Joe Baker . . . 42 goals.

258 Davie Shaw, Eddie Turnbull and Ally McLeod.

259 Pat Stanton.

260 Dunfermline 5 Hibernian 6.

261 1977.

262 Sportswear firm, Bukta.

263 Neil Martin on 22 March 1965 . . . Hibs won 4-2.

264 Stranraer.

265 Malta.

266 Clyde.

267 Nigeria.

268 Gordon Rae (signed from Whitehill Welfare in 1977).

269 8-1 v Kilmarnock (h) 2 April 1983.

270 1938.

271 In aid of the Willie Ormond Memorial Cup.

272 Dave Ewing.

273 Bobby Johnstone.

274 Durban City.

275 Jim O'Rourke.

276 Alan Wells, at Hibs versus Swansea in 1980, fresh from a 100-metres victory in the 1980 Moscow Olympics.

277 *B*: 95,123.

278 Eddie Turnbull and Willie Ormond.

279 St Johnstone.

280 He won a Premier League Championship Winner's medal

with Celtic and a First Division Champs medal with Hibs
. . . in the same season!

281 Queen of the South.
282 Drumcondra.
283 Alan Gordon.
284 Ian Hendry . . . he broke a leg within the first 20 seconds of his debut and didn't play for Hibs again.
285 Sir Matt Busby.
286 Peter Cormack and an own goal from a nice fellow called Zoco.
287 Ian St John of Motherwell.
288 Morton.
289 They announced that Hibernian had bought Easter Road from Edinburgh District Council.
290 Steve Cowan with 30 goals (28 in domestic competitions and two in a challenge match).
291 *100 Years of Hibs*.
292 John MacKay.
293 Stewart Brown.
294 Eddie Turnbull.
295 Murdoch.
296 In season 1976/77 they drew 18 of their 36 Premier League fixtures.
297 Sir John Bruce.
298 Paul McGovern (Morton 1 Hibernian 1).
299 Distillery.
300 Walter Galbraith.
301 Airdrie . . . Hibs won 2-1 on 4 April 1964.
302 Bob Shankly.
303 Alan Gordon.
304 Because a fire had damaged the Hampden stand.
305 Celtic won 6-2.
306 Dundee.
307 Raith Rovers and Hamilton Academical.

308 Ally McLeod.
309 Blackburn Rovers.
310 Season 1961/62.

311 *Left to right* . . . Stevenson, Quinn, Hunter, O'Rourke, Scott, Allan, Marinello, Stanton, McBride, Davis, Blackley, McGraw, Grant, Shevlane, Madsen and Cormack.
312 Alex Scott.
313 Joe Davis.
314 Quinn, Hunter, O'Rourke, Marinello and McBride.
315 Eric Stevenson, Thomson Allan, Chris Shevlane, Peter Marinello and Peter Cormack (Cormack a ground staff boy at Tynecastle in 1962).
316 Allan McGraw, Chris Shevlane and John Madsen.
317 Pat Quinn (East Fife), Willie Hunter (Queen of the South), Pat Stanton (Cowdenbeath, Dunfermline and Hibernian), John Blackley (Hamilton Academical player/manager, Hibernian and Cowdenbeath), Allan McGraw (Morton) and Peter Cormack (Partick Thistle and Anorthosis in Cyprus).

318 Iain Munro (left) and Ally MacLeod.
319 St Mirren from Paisley (St Mirren also known as the "Saints").

320 Hull City.
321 Seville (1986 friendly).

322 Berwick Rangers.
323 Leicester City.
324 Arbroath.
325 Preston North End.
326 Oldham Athletic.
327 Brechin City.
328 Barcelona (have since moved to Nou Camp).
329 Bristol City.
330 Alloa Athletic.
331 Nottingham Forest. (Hibs played the English club in the Vancouver stadium on 1965 Canadian tour.)
332 Stirling Albion.
333 Third Lanark. (They folded in 1967.)
334 Middlesbrough.
335 Elgin City.
336 Juventus (Italy).
337 Hamburg (West Germany).
338 Cowdenbeath.
339 Napoli (Italy).
340 Newcastle United.
341 Olympia Ljubljana (Yugoslavia).
342 Wigan Athletic (1971 friendly . . . Wigan non-League at the time).
343 Porto (Portugal).
344 Liverpool.
345 Sheffield United.
346 Derby County.
347 Forfar Athletic.
348 Doncaster Rovers.
349 Grimsby Town.
350 York City.
351 Blackburn Rovers.
352 East Stirlingshire.
353 Bury.
354 Huddersfield Town.
355 Manchester City.
356 Stenhousemuir.
357 Ayr United.

358 Left to right . . . Gordon Hunter, Mickey Weir, Alan Sneddon and Dave McKellar.

359 Jim O'Rourke (10).
360 B: 32.

361 Blackley rejoined the club as assistant manager.

362 Left to right: Jim Black, John Brownlie and Willie McEwan.

HIBEES IN HIDING

363 Linwood (Alex).
364 Mick McManus.
365 Spalding (Derek).
366 Another Alex Cameron.
367 Jim Blair.
368 Jackie McNamara.
369 Bobby and John Baxter.
370 Wren (Jackie).
371 Martin (Neil).
372 Former chairman, Harry Swan.
373 Collins (John) . . . Celt, Bobby and actress, Joan.
374 Fox (Desmond).
375 The Hunters (Willie and Gordon).
376 Carroll (Pat).

377 Herriot (Jim) . . . ex-World Lightweight Champion, Jim Watt, being the other half.
378 Parke (John).
379 Gareth Evans.
380 Mervyn Jones.
381 Welsh (Peter).
382 Hamilton Handling.
383 Willie Irvine times two.
384 Cousin (Alan).
385 Souness (Jimmy).
386 Callaghan (Patrick).
387 Rice (Brian).
388 Preston (Tommy).
389 Joe Davis.
390 John Grant and Dougie Bell.
391 Farm (George).
392 Johnny Aitkenhead.
393 Fulton (Mark).
394 Rikki Fleming.
395 Pringle (Alex).
396 Willie Miller.
397 Stein (Colin).

PICTURE QUIZ – TONY HIGGINS

398 On 28 May 1979 Tony scored Hibs' first goal in the 2nd replay of the Scottish Cup final at Hampden.
399 August 1973 in the semi-final of the Drybrough Cup. (Hibs won 2-1 at Easter Road.)
400 Partick Thistle, Morton and Stranraer.

PICTURE QUIZ

401 Jim O'Rourke.
402 Holy Cross Academy.
403 A: 10.
404 St Johnstone.

PICTURE QUIZ – JACKIE McNAMARA

405 Versus Dundee United at Easter Road, 4 September 1976 (Hibs lost 1-2).

406 Irish League. (Scottish League won 4-2 at Windsor Park).

407 Hibs 0 Newcastle United 3.

PICTURE QUIZ

408 Fulham.

409 C: £50,000.

410 33 years old.

411 Patrick Thistle and Hibs won 2-1.

EUROPEAN COMPETITION

412 Rot-Weiss Essen (West Germany). Hibs won 4-0 in Essen and drew 1-1 at home (European Cup 1955-56).

413 Joe McBride v Lokomotiv Leipzig (Fairs Cup 1968/69).

414 Hibernian's 4-4 draw with mighty Barcelona in Spain.

415 Baker (2), McLeod and Preston.

416 Sandor Kocsis and Ladislav Kubala.

417 Hibernian 3 Barcelona 2 . . . Bobby Kinloch scored the winner from the spot.

418 He scored two Fairs Cup goals v Copenhagen in the Danish capital.

419 Hibs won 3-2 in Copenhagen and 4-0 at Easter Road.

420 Hibs' 5-0 victory over Italians, Napoli, in the 2nd leg of a Fairs Cup tie.

421 Hibs became the first Scottish side in eight attempts to master Italian opposition in a two-leg contest.

422 José Altafini. (Napoli won 4-1.)

423 Dino Zoff.

424 He played in the Juventus side which won 4-2 at Easter Road in the UEFA Cup. (The Italians won 8-2 on aggregate . . . least said!)

425 Duncan Falconer.

426 Gerry Baker and Morris Stevenson scored the goals in a 2-1 win with Jimmy O'Rourke the young debutant.

427 Stade Rheims . . . 0-3. (0-2 away and 0-1 at home).

428 Raymond Kopa.

429 Sochaux 1976/77 UEFA Cup and Racing Strasbourg 1978/79 UEFA Cup.

430 Lausanne Sports.

431 Sporting Lisbon.

432 Hibs lost 2-1 probably due to the fact that they were wearing a purple and white strip.

433 Hibs 6 Sporting Lisbon 1.

434 1-1.

435 Ronnie Allen.

436 Rosenborg Trondheim (Norway) 12-3 UEFA Cup 1974/75.

437 Hibs won 9-1 at Easter Road.

438 Swedes, Djurgaarden, were forced to play both matches in Scotland due to the severity of the Swedish winter.

439 Hibs won 3-1 in Glasgow and 1-0 in Edinburgh with Eddie Turnbull scoring from the spot in both matches.

440 Jim O'Rourke scored yet another hat-trick, this time versus Besa from Albania.

441 Alan Gordon v Hajduk Split (Yugoslavia).

442 Hibs won 4-2 at home and lost 0-3 away.

443 Hamburg.

444 Hibs lost 0-1 in Germany and won 2-1 in Edinburgh with the great Uwe Seeler getting the goal which really mattered.

445 Joe McBride (Hibs won 9-2 on aggregate).

446 Belenenses . . . Hibs drew 3-3 at home and won 3-1 away.

447 John Fraser.

448 Sochaux, John Brownlie.

449 Valencia (Spain), Leeds United and Liverpool.

450 Roma (Italy).

451 Hibernian won 2-0 at home and lost 1-2 away.

452 Johnny Graham.

453 Alex Cropley (v Rosenborg Trondheim, 2 October 1974).

454 Jack Charlton (Hibs lost 2-1 on aggregate).

455 Pat Stanton.

456 0-0 . . . Leeds won 5-4 on penalties.

457 Versus Rheims 1955/56, Red Star 1961/62 and Liverpool
1970/71.

458 John Toshack.

459 Hibs won 1-0 in Edinburgh and lost 1-3 in Liverpool.

460 That menace . . . Toshack!

461 Alex Edwards.

462 Keflavik (UEFA 1973/74 . . . Hibs won 3-1 on aggregate).

463 Jim Black and Tony Higgins.

464 Norrköping.

465 Joe McBride and Alan Gordon . . . eight goals apiece.

466 Olympia Ljubljana (aggregate 5-1).

467 Joe Davis . . . both penalties!

468 Peter Cormack (2) and Eric Stevenson.

469 Joe Davis with yet another penalty!

470 Willie Muirhead.

471 Simpson was reserve goalkeeper for the Scottish League v
the Italian League and, despite the fact that Hibs were
desperate that he play in Belgrade, Scottish League officials
refused to release him.

472 John McNamee . . . Hibs won 2-0.

473 Valencia 2 Hibs 0.

474 Valencia won 3-0 on their ground.

475 Racing Strasbourg (France). Hibs lost 0-2 away and won 1-0
at home.

PICTURE QUIZ

476 *Left to right* . . . Trainer Sammy Kean, Davie Shaw, Peter
Aird, Hugh Howie, Gordon Smith, Willie Ormond and
Eddie Turnbull.

PICTURE QUIZ

477 *Left to right* . . . Trainer Eddie Turnbull, Jock Buchanan,
John Baxter, Joe McLelland, John Frye and Duncan
Falconer.

478 Ferenc Puskas of Real Madrid.

479 John Deans (Celtic).

480 Southampton.

481 Ayr United.

482 Newcastle United.

483 Swansea City.

484 Willie Groves.

485 Airdrieonians . . . also known as "The Waysiders".

486 Third Lanark.

487 Alloa Athletic . . . Hibs won 11-2 in a record League Cup victory.

488 Forfar Athletic.

489 Stenhousemuir.

490 Montrose . . . Hibs lost 1-0 first leg advantage when beaten 3-1 away.

491 Everton.

492 "The Trotters".

493 Crystal Palace.

494 Celtic.

495 Birmingham City.

496 Arbroath.

497 West Bromwich Albion.

498 Gordon Durie was transferred to Chelsea.

499 Juventus.

500 George McCluskey. He scored the only goal of 1980 final for Celtic v Rangers.

501 Huddersfield Town.

502 Hull City.

503 *Turnbull's Tornadoes* on one side of the disc and *Hibernian Give us a Goal* on the other.

504 *Back row left to right* . . . Duncan, Schaedler and Gordon. *Middle row left to right* . . . Blackley, Black, Stanton, Hazel and O'Rourke. *Front row left to right* . . . Herriot, Cropley, Edwards and Brownlie.

505 Johnny Hamilton.

PICTURE QUIZ

506 Goalkeeper, Ronnie Simpson.

TRANSFERS

507 Stoke City.
508 Colin Stein . . . from Hibs to Rangers for £100,000 in October 1968.
509 C: Dundee United.
510 Joe Harper.
511 John Madsen.
512 Jimmy Kerr.
513 Pat Quinn.
514 Willie Hunter.
515 Ally Scott and Graham Fyfe.
516 Peter Wilson.
517 Alex Linwood.
518 Hibs tell me it was £36,000 + VAT.
519 Deveronvale.
520 Johnny McLeod . . . Arsenal.
521 Neil Martin . . . Transferred to Sunderland for £45,000, Neil moved again when Coventry paid £90,000 for his services in February 1968.
522 Thomson Allan joined Dundee.
523 East Fife.
524 Bobby Thomson.
525 Graham Harvey.
526 Dunfermline . . . just one of nine senior clubs for which Joe played!
527 Davie Gibson.
528 Mark Caughey.

529 Joe McLelland.
530 West Ham United.
531 Leslie Johnston.
532 It was the first five-figure fee paid for a Scot and by a Scottish club.
533 Stuart.
534 Sunderland.
535 £60,000.
536 John Connolly.
537 Sammy Baird.
538 Tommy Leishman.
539 Hamilton Academical.
540 Stan Vincent.
541 C: Tranmere Rovers.
542 John Grant.
543 Joe Ward.
544 Alex Cropley.
545 Willie Miller.
546 Motherwell.
547 Airdrieonians.
548 Jim McArthur.
549 Arsenal.
550 It was the then record fee paid for a goalkeeper (£4,500).
551 Jackie Plenderleith.
552 Billy Kirkwood and Stuart Beedie.
553 Manchester City . . . Ipswich Town.
554 Jim Herriot.
555 Dundee United.
556 Bobby Hutchinson.
557 Stirling Albion.
558 Arbroath.
559 Morton.
560 Third Lanark.
561 Falkirk.
562 Crystal Palace.
563 St Johnstone.
564 Montrose.
565 St Johnstone.

566 Dundee United.
567 Clydebank.

568 Willie Toner.

569 Hutchison Vale.
570 Liverpool.
571 Falkirk (player/manager), Stoke City and Leeds United.
572 24 times, (eight with Hibs).
573 Public Relations Officer.
574 He was President of the SFA.

575 Joe McBride.
576 Kirkintilloch Rob Roy.
577 Jim Easton.
578 Dundee.

579 St Mirren in the Drybrough Cup (Hibs won 2-1).
580 Dunfermline Athletic (Hibs won 5-1).
581 Seven.
582 Dundee United.
583 Dunfermline Athletic.

584 Matt Busby, Willie Ormond and Ally McLeod.
585 Alex Cropley.

586 Jimmy Dunn.

587 Bobby Atherton v Ireland and England in 1899.

588 Willie Harper, (England 1 Scotland 1).

589 Alan Rough in 1986.

590 Willie Miller (Celtic) in 1947, George Farm (Blackpool) in 1953, Tommy Younger (Liverpool) in 1957, Ronnie Simpson (Celtic) in 1967 and Jim Herriot (Birmingham City) in 1969.

591 Arthur Duncan in 1975.

592 Saudi Arabia.

593 Joe Harper scored the only goal of the match v Denmark, 3 September 1975.

594 Des Bremner.

595 Holland.

596 John Blackley, (Scotland won 3-1).

597 Harry Ritchie.

598 On each occasion Hibs had the same five players in the Scottish eleven. Govan, Shaw, Smith, Combe and Turnbull.

599 The United States of America.

600 George Stewart.

601 Robert Neil.

602 Lindsay Muir.

603 Pat Stanton.

604 Finland and Poland.

605 Paddy Farrell.

606 Michael Gallagher.

607 Jack Jones and William Gowdy.

608 Hugh Howie . . . (Wales 1 Scotland 3).

609 Lawrie Reilly.

610 James Main.

611 Yugoslavia, Austria and Hungary (Scottish tour).

612 United States of America, (6-0).

613 Harry Rennie.

614 Willie Ormond (1954), Eddie Turnbull (1958) and John Blackley (1974).

615 Jack Reilly.

616 Jimmy Caskie.

617 Willie Bogan.

618 Norway.

PICTURE QUIZ

619 Neil Martin.

WHO'S WHO?

620 Gordon Chisholm.

621 John McNamee.

622 Jimmy McColl.

623 Cecil Graham.

624 Jock Govan.

625 Hugh Howie.

626 Duncan Urquhart.

627 Bobby Flavell.

628 Ronnie Simpson . . . first capped v England in 1967 when aged 36.

629 George Farm.

630 Davie Gibson.

631 Lawrie Leslie. Incidentally, Leicester won 4-3 on aggregate.

632 Bobby Templeton.

633 Hugh Whyte.

634 Brian McGinley.

635 Mike Conroy.

636 Willie Jamieson . . . Brora Rangers.

637 Peter Kerr.

638 John Paterson.

639 Ian Crawford.

640 Sparkes (Raymond).

641 Mickey Weir.

642 Robin Rae.

643 Davie Laing.

644 Billy McLaren.

645 *Back row left to right* . . . Smith, Spalding, McArthur, Bremner and O'Rourke. *Middle row left to right* . . . Manager Turnbull, coach Humphries, Blackley, McGregor, Higgins, Brownlie, Black, Fraser and Auld (both coaches). *Front row left to right* . . . Edwards, Schaedler, Munro, Stanton, Gordon, Cropley, Duncan and trainer/physio McNiven.

646 Alex Edwards . . . he played in the Dunfermline side which beat Hearts 3-1 at Hampden in 1968.

647 Bertie Auld won three with Celtic and manager Turnbull's assistant, Wilson Humphries, scored one of Motherwell's four goals in the 1952 final v Dundee.

648 Erich Schaedler.

649 Jim Black.

ENOUGH TO GIVE YOU NIGHTMARES

650 Dundee United . . . George McCluskey and Andy Watson.

651 Oesters Vaxjoe . . . Oesters 4 Hibs 1.

652 Season 1959/60.

653 Raith Rovers.

654 Hearts 5 Hibernian 0.

655 Six . . . Thirds 6 Hibernian 1.

656 Wigan Athletic.

657 Nuremberg.

658 Dundee . . . final score also 4-0.

659 East Fife, who won 2-0 after drawing 0-0 at Easter Road.

660 Hearts 6 Hibs 1.

661 Hibernian 1 Hamilton 3.

662 John Brogan.

663 Celtic, who won 6-1.

664 Meadowbank Thistle.

665 Bury, who beat Hibs 4-0.

666 Dunfermline Athletic.

667 Gerry Mayes.

668 Motherwell, who won 3-2.

669 Rangers 10 Hibernian 0 . . . The worst defeat in the history of the club and too horrific to contemplate. I think we've had enough of this torture!

KIDDIES' KORNER

670 *Left to right* . . . Paul Kane, Gordon Rae, Andy Goram, Gordon Hunter, Mickey Weir and Gareth Evans.

671 Gordon Rae.

672 Andy Goram, Mickey Weir and Gareth Evans.

673 Oldham Athletic, Luton Town and Rotherham.

674 Willie McEwan.

675 Peter Cormack.

676 Eddie May.

677 John Collins.

678 Alan Sneddon.

679 Gordon Rae.

680 Graham Mitchell.

681 Gordon Hunter.

682 Paul Kane.

683 Gareth Evans.

684 Mickey Weir.

685 Graham Mitchell.

686 Alan Sneddon.

687 Andy Goram.

688 Gordon Rae.

689 Falkirk.

690 Dundee United.

691 Dunfermline Athletic.

692 Dumbarton (Scottish Cup).

693 Morton.

694 Motherwell.

695 Aberdeen.

696 Dundee.

697 St Mirren.

698 Celtic.
699 Andy Watson.
700 Neil Orr.
701 Calum Milne.
702 Andy Watson.
703 Joe Tortolano.
704 Eddie May.

705 Jim O'Rourke.

706 George Stewart.
707 Hibernian 2 Hearts 1.

DERBY DAZE

708 Christmas Day 1875. Hearts won 1-0.
709 24 February 1877.
710 1-0 for Hibs, played at the Meadows.
711 1896 . . . Hearts 3 Hibs 1.
712 It was played at Logie Green in Edinburgh . . . the only final in the history of the competition to be played outside Glasgow.
713 They agreed that, whatever transpired, there would be no after-match protest.
714 Middlesbrough.
715 James McGhee, Willie McCartney and Willie Ormond.
716 Tommy McIntyre 10 September 1938, Lawrie Reilly 20 September 1952 and Pat Quinn 9 September 1967.
717 Joe Baker . . . Hearts 3 Hibernian 4.
718 Hearts 0 Hibernian 4 (also final score).
719 O'Rourke (2) and Stevenson (2).
720 Roddy McDonald.

721 Richard Harker, Gordon Smith, Alan Gordon and Ralph Callachan.

722 O'Rourke (2), Gordon (2), Duncan (2) and Cropley.

723 Hibs 3 Hearts 1 . . . first home League victory over Hearts for 14 years.

724 Joe Davies (penalty) . . . first time in 20 years that Hibs won a New Year fixture at Easter Road.

725 Pat Stanton (1-1).

726 Joe Harper.

727 Ally MacLeod.

728 Hibs 3 Hearts 0 . . . Duncan (2) and Smith.

729 The Tom Hart Memorial Trophy.

730 Jackie McNamara.

731 John Hazel . . . Arthur Duncan scored the other goal in a 2-1 win.

732 Gordon Smith . . . 14 goals for Hibs between 1941 and 1951.

733 Tommy Preston.

734 The Skol Festival Trophy.

735 Hibs won because they had won seven corners to Hearts' six corners.

736 Willie Paterson.

737 Aston Villa won the Allison Challenge Cup with a 4-3 win at Tynecastle.

738 Eddie May.

739 Aberdeen beat them 2-0 at Pittodrie . . . Hearts were in the First Division.

740 Joe McBride.

741 August: Hibs 1 Hearts 3. November: Hearts 1 Hibs 1.

742 George McCluskey and Mickey Weir.

PICTURE QUIZ

743 *Left to right* . . . Gordon Smith, Tommy Younger, John Paterson, Jock Govan (half hidden), Hugh Howie and Jimmy Souness.

744 Rapide Vienna (3-2).

745 Bayern 1 Hibernian 6.

746 Hibs played Arsenal at Highbury in October 1952 in aid of the National Playing Fields Association and the Central Council of Physical Recreation.

747 *Left to right* . . . Tommy Younger, Gordon Smith, Michael Gallagher, John Paterson, Bobby Combe and Bobby Johnstone.

748 Say it quietly! Arsenal 7 Hibernian 1 . . . and to make matters worse it was televised live!

749 Lawrie Reilly.

FRIENDLIES, TESTIMONIALS AND TOURS

750 Lawrie Reilly and Nat Lofthouse.

751 Hibs 5 Bolton 2.

752 Czechoslovakia.

753 Rapide Vienna (they won 5-3 in 1951 and 2-1 in 1954).

754 Jock Buchanan (Johnny McLeod got the other).

755 3-0.

756 Hibs won 2-0 and Gordon Durie scored both goals.

757 Barcelona.

758 Maastricht.

759 Hibs 1 Liverpool 2, and Billy Liddell scored the second goal for the visitors.

760 Willie Ormond, Joe Baker and Gordon Smith.

761 He scored all Hibs' goals in a 5-0 win.

762 Concordia.

763 Ottawa 0 Hibs 15.

764 Nottingham Forest . . . Hibs won 2-1.

765 Willie Jamieson.

766 Bruce Rioch scored the winner for the "Rams".

767 He scored a hat-trick in a 3-3 draw.

768 San José Earthquakes . . . Hibs won 3-1.

769 George Best and Jimmy Gabriel.

770 Feyenoord.

771 Hibernian 4 Leeds United 4.

772 John Charles.

773 Hibernian 5 Manchester United 0.
774 Gornik.
775 They were the first Continental side to win at Easter Road since Barcelona in 1962.
776 York City 2 Hibernian 1.
777 Spurs 2 Hibs 5.
778 Tottenham 0 Hibernian 1.
779 It was an own goal scored by none other than Alf Ramsey . . . nice man!
780 Spurs 1 Hibs 2.
781 Hibernian 1 Tottenham 5.
782 Hibs won 5-2 and Joe Baker scored a hat-trick.
783 To hansel their floodlights . . . Doncaster 0 Hibs 3.
784 Manchester City 1 Hibernian 4.
785 Jimmy Souness, who scored all four Hibs goals.
786 Manchester United 1 Hibernian 1.
787 Parke and McNamee.
788 Milorad Nizetic.
789 Willie Irvine (Mark Two).
790 Hibs 3 Notts Forest 2 . . . Joe Baker scored both Forest's goals.
791 Cork Hibs . . . the real Hibs beat them 2-0 during an Eire tour.
792 Seville, managed by Jock Wallace, beat Hibs 2-1 at Easter Road and 2-0 in Spain.
793 Joe Baker . . . Hibernian 6 Middlesbrough 6.
794 Brian Clough.
795 Middlesbrough 3 Hibernian 4.
796 Celtic . . . Hibs 6 Celtic 3.
797 Portsmouth.
798 Hibernian 2 Celtic 1.
799 Pat Stanton of course . . . arouses some suspicion, especially when it is noted that big Tony Higgins was involved in the incident which led to the spot kick.
800 Newcastle United.
801 Crystal Palace.
802 Vasco da Gama.
803 Toronto.

804 Bangu.

805 The Houston Astrodome.

806 FA Cupholders, Manchester United.

807 Hibernian 3 Sunderland 0.

808 Hibs 1 Sunderland 2 . . . Gordon Chisholm.

809 Iain Munro.

810 Versus Stenhousemuir at Ochilview in November 1951 (Hibs won 5-3).

811 Hearts beat Hibs 2-0 in October 1954.

812 Reading.

813 Hibernian 9 Scotland XI 3.

814 Hibs 3 International XI 4 . . . Charlie Nicholas.

PICTURE QUIZ

815 *Left to right* . . . McIntyre, McLean, Milne, Kean and Nutley.

PICTURE QUIZ

816 *Back row left to right* . . . Shaw, Govan, Kerr, Howie, Aird and Kean. *Front row left to right* . . . Smith, Finnegan, Cuthbertson, Turnbull and Ormond.

PICTURE QUIZ

817 Joe McBride.

818 Young Joe became a Hibee when signed from Oldham Athletic.

PICTURE QUIZ

819 Eddie Turnbull is fourth from the right in the front row.

820 In the middle row goalkeeper Bobby Brown is third from the left and George Young sixth from the left.

821 *C*: Queen of the South.

PICTURE QUIZ – GORDON SMITH

822 Smith joined Hibs from Dundee North End in April 1941.
823 Two weeks after joining the club Smith played in the Hibs side which beat Hearts 5-3 in a Southern League match.
824 He scored five times . . . a Scottish record for a winger in a League match.
825 *B*: 364 goals.
826 He played in 18 full internationals and made his debut v Northern Ireland at Hampden in November 1946 (0-0).
827 English Champions Manchester United, and Hibs won 7-3.
828 1951.
829 Against Third Lanark at Cathkin on 14 March 1959 (Thirds won 2-1 in a Scottish Cup-tie.)

PICTURE QUIZ – BOBBY JOHNSTONE

830 Newtongrange Star.
831 17 times (13 times while a Hibs player).
832 Against England at Wembley in 1951 . . . Bobby scored one of the Scottish goals in a 3-2 win.
833 *B*: £22,000.
834 He scored in consecutive FA Cup finals, 1-3 v Newcastle in 1955 and 3-1 v Birmingham City in 1956. Bobby obviously enjoyed playing on the lush green grass of Wembley.
835 In September 1959 for £6,000.
836 Oldham Athletic.

PICTURE QUIZ – LAWRIE REILLY

837 He joined Hibs in 1945 from Edinburgh Thistle.
838 C: 187 goals.
839 38 times.
840 Five (a Scottish record).
841 1953 when "Last-Minute Reilly" equalised with his second goal in the dying seconds of the match.
842 Outside-left.
843 Motherwell . . . Reilly scored four in a 7-3 victory at Fir Park and three in Hibs' 7-2 win at Easter Road.
844 He was the only one never on the payroll of any other club in any capacity.
845 Rangers.
846 Hibs 3 Rangers 1 . . . Aitken, Baxter and Reilly.

PICTURE QUIZ – EDDIE TURNBULL

847 In 1946 from Forth Rangers.
848 Eight times.
849 Versus Belgium at Hampden in 1948, (2-0).
850 Celtic (Hibs won 4-1).
851 C: eight times.
852 Right-half.
853 Club trainer.
854 Queen's Park.
855 July 1971.
856 April 1980.

PICTURE QUIZ – WILLIE ORMOND

857 Stenhousemuir.
858 He was the only player signed from another senior club . . . changed days!
859 Six times.
860 Versus Roma in Italy in a 1961 Fairs Cup tie.

861 He returned to Easter Road in Falkirk's colours and scored both his side's goals in a 2-2 draw.
862 St Johnstone, Hearts and Hibernian.
863 January 1973.
864 He was awarded the OBE.
865 Coach/scout (becoming manager a month later).

PICTURE QUIZ – JOE BAKER

866 Liverpool.
867 True . . . he played in the dark blue against England and Wales and scored three goals.
868 Chelsea.
869 Eight times (five times with Hibs), and he scored one of England's goals in a 2-1 victory over Northern Ireland at Wembley in 1959.
870 A: 159.
871 Joe scored five Christmas Eve goals v Third Lanark in an 8-4 win.
872 Nine.
873 £65,000.
874 Denis Law.
875 Hibs, Torino, Arsenal, Notts Forest, Sunderland, Hibs (again) and Raith Rovers.
876 January 1971 . . . scoring Hibs' second goal in a 2-1 win over Aberdeen.

PICTURE QUIZ – WILLIE HAMILTON

877 B: £6,000.
878 Versus Finland, 27 May 1965 (Finland 1, Scotland 2).
879 Versus Ottawa All Stars in 1965 tour of Canada.
880 Versus Rangers (Hibs won 2-1).
881 Sheffield United, Aston Villa, Middlesbrough, Hearts (twice) and Hibernian.
882 Aston Villa.

PICTURE QUIZ – PAT STANTON

883 Walter Galbraith.

884 Versus Motherwell (Motherwell won 4-3).

885 Versus Clyde, 3 November 1973.

886 Sixteen times.

887 Versus Holland at Hampden in 1966.

888 1970.

889 Jackie McNamara.

890 Cowdenbeath and Dunfermline.

891 September 1982.

892 September 1984.

893 Tommy Docherty.

PICTURE QUIZ – PETER CORMACK

894 Versus Airdrie at Broomfield, 24 November 1962 (Hibs lost 1-2).

895 Nine times (four as a Hibs player).

896 Versus Brazil at Hampden in 1966 (1-1).

897 Aberdeen . . . Hibs won 6-2 at Pittodrie.

898 Nottingham Forest.

899 Liverpool and Bristol City.

900 Versus Dundee United at Tannadice, 23 February 1980 (Hibs lost 0-1).

901 January 1987.

902 Bristol City.

PICTURE QUIZ – JOHN BLACKLEY

903 Gairdoch United.

904 Seven times.

905 Versus Czechoslovakia (a)in a 1973 World Cup Qualifier.

906 C: £100,000.

907 Preston North End and Hamilton Academical.

908 October 1984.
909 November 1986.
910 He came on to the pitch last and kicked a ball into his own net before each game started.

PICTURE QUIZ – JOHN BROWNLIE

911 Pumpherston Juniors.
912 Seven times.
913 Russia (a) 1971 . . . John became the youngest ever Hibs player to be capped at full international level for Scotland (aged 19 years 95 days).
914 Ralph Callachan.
915 Middlesbrough, Hartlepool United and Berwick Rangers.

PICTURE QUIZ – ARTHUR DUNCAN

916 Partick Thistle.
917 Falkirk (Hibs won 6-0).
918 Unbelievably, Arthur's former club were beating Celtic 4-0 in the League Cup final.
919 St Johnstone (a) . . . it was the first hat-trick scored by a Hibs player in the new Premier League set-up. (Hibs won 4-3).
920 Six times.
921 Versus Portugal (sub), 13 May 1975. (Scotland won 1-0 at Hampden).
922 Meadowbank Thistle.

PICTURE QUIZ – ALLY MacLEOD

923 The Irish League in Belfast.
924 A: 99 times.
925 True . . . from season 1976/77 to season 1980/81.
926 Leicester City.
927 Dundee United.

928 . . . "Sleezy".
929 . . . "Onion".
930 . . . "Shades".
931 . . . "Niddrie".
932 . . . "Cilla".
933 . . . "Sloop".
934 . . . "Mickey".
935 . . . "Rourkie".
936 . . . "Tosh".
937 . . . "Sodjer".
938 . . . "Flyer".
939 . . . "Cannonball" or "Ned".

PICTURE QUIZ

940 *Back row left to right* . . . Mitchell, Hunter, McIntyre, Chisholm, McCluskey, Sneddon and Cowan. *Middle row left to right* . . . Coach Ferguson, Tortolano, May, Rough, Milne, Kane and coach Stevenson. *Front row left to right* . . . Manager Miller, Weir, Collins, Rae, Smith, McBride and Assistant Manager Cormack.
941 Gordon Hunter, Calum Milne, Paul Kane, Mickey Weir, John Collins and Gordon Rae.
942 Tommy McIntyre and Steve Cowan.
943 Bobby Smith.
944 George McCluskey.

PICTURE QUIZ

945 Grant, Leslie, Baxter, Fraser, Aitken and Preston.
946 McLeod, Paterson and Reilly.

947 Season 1970/71.

948 *Back row left to right* . . . Hazel, Shevlane, Brownlie, Meikle, Marshall, Allan, Baines, Black, McEwan, R. Duncan and coach Fraser. *Middle row left to right* . . . Trainer/physio McNiven, D. Grant, Nelson, Ness, O'Rourke, Jones, Gillet, Gordon, Schaedler, C. Grant, Stanton, Pringle, Blackley and manager McFarlane. *Front row left to right* . . . A. Duncan, Lyall, Hamilton, Cropley, Blair, Graham, Murphy, McBride, Young, Hunter and Stevenson.

949 Alex Cropley and goalkeepers Gordon Marshall and Roy Baines.

950 *Back row left to right* . . . Trainer/physio McNiven, Turnbull, Connolly, McArthur, G. Murray, MacLeod. *Middle row left to right* . . . Coach Lambie, Callachan, Jamieson, Donaldson, Paterson, Brazil and assistant manager Quinn. *Front row left to right* . . . Duncan, Hendry, McNamara, manager Auld, Sneddon, Rae and Rodier.

951 First Division championship trophy won in season 1980/81.

952 Stuart Turnbull, Willie Jamieson and Ally Brazil.

953 Bertie Auld and John Lambie.

954 *Left to right* . . . Gordon Smith, Bobby Johnstone, Jimmy McColl, Lawrie Reilly, Johnny Halligan, Eddie Turnbull and Willie Ormond. The "Famous Five" and 1920's team-mate Johnny Halligan presented McColl with a gold watch to mark his 50 years of marvellous service to the club.

171

955 Johnny McLeod and John Parke.

956 Ronnie Simpson and Bertie Auld (Celtic), George Best (Manchester United) and Des Bremner (Aston Villa).

957 Hector Nicol.

958 The Hearts song . . . *"The Boys in Maroon"*.

959 Jock Weir.

960 Neil Martin.

961 West Bromwich Albion.

962 Joe McBride.

963 It ended a 12-year wait for two points in an Easter Road League match v Celtic.

964 Former chairman, Harry Swan.

965 Ken Buchanan, fresh from a world lightweight title defence against Ismael Laguna in New York's Madison Square Gardens.

966 Willie Temperley.

967 Season 1964/65.

968 It was the first season in which Hibs had achieved a League double over Rangers since Hibs' Championship-winning season in 1902/03.

969 George Stewart.

970 Queen of the South.

971 Thomas Allan. He was loaned to Meadowbank in 1979 while a Dundee player.

972 Jim Brown (3-3).

973 Isak Refvik in Israel versus a Tel Aviv XI (1-1).

974 Svein Mathisen.

975 Gary Murray.

976 Alan Rough.

977 Gordon Rae.

978 Newcastle United.

979 Celtic.

980 Ally McLeod . . . Johnny Hamilton.

981 George McCluskey. (Celtic won 2-1.)

982 Stuart Rae.

983 Willie Murray.

984 John Fraser and John Baxter.
985 Versus Aberdeen at Pittodrie in August 1985 (the Dons won 3-0).
986 Johnny Cuthbertson.
987 Graham Mitchell.
988 Bobby Hutchinson.
989 Stuart Beedie and Steve Cowan . . . Graeme Souness was, of course, the fellow sent off. (Hibs won 2-1.)
990 Dundee Hibernians became Dundee United in October 1923.
991 Peter Welsh.
992 Mickey Weir.
993 Bertie Auld.
994 Having achieved a shut-out in the previous 12 League matches, it was unlucky 13 when Stanton and Baker scored in a 2-1 win for Hibs.
995 Hibs daft . . . Jimmy returned to Easter Road in St Johnstone's colours and scored the only goal of the game.
996 Motherwell . . . Hibs won 7-3 (a) and 7-2 (h).
997 Bobby Duncan.
998 Hamilton Academical.
999 East Fife.
1000 Willie Temperley.
1001 Tony Higgins.
1002 Hugh Hamil.
1003 Edinburgh City.
1004 August 1978.
1005 Rangers.
1006 Preston North End.
1007 Kenny Waugh.
1008 Accrington Stanley, Bradford PA, New Brighton and Tranmere Rovers.
1009 Dumbarton.
1010 Carlisle United.
1011 Scott and Martin.
1012 John Frye.
1013 Johnny McLeod.
1014 Gerry Baker.

1015 William Harrower.

1016 Celtic.

1017 East Fife.

1018 Blackpool.

PICTURE QUIZ

1019 The late, great Erich Schaedler.

PICTURE QUIZ

1020 *Back row left to right* . . . Gillet, Blackley, Bobby Duncan and Black. *Front row left to right* . . . Hamilton, Graham, McEwan, Jones, the great man himself, Hunter, Stanton and Stevenson.

FINAL WHISTLE

1021 Chairman David Duff, at the launch of the sponsorship deal with the Frank Graham Group. . . . *Yes, the "giant" is, indeed, beginning to stir, and frightening days lie ahead for the opposition. Chairman David Duff, managing director, Jim Gray, manager Alex Miller, and everyone at Easter Road are doing a grand job . . . but, more than anything, they need the backing of the fans! Together, and through a concerted effort, everyone who loves "The Hibees" can play their part in helping to breathe life into this wonderful football club which is called HIBERNIAN!*